汉英对照 CHINESE-ENGLISH READER

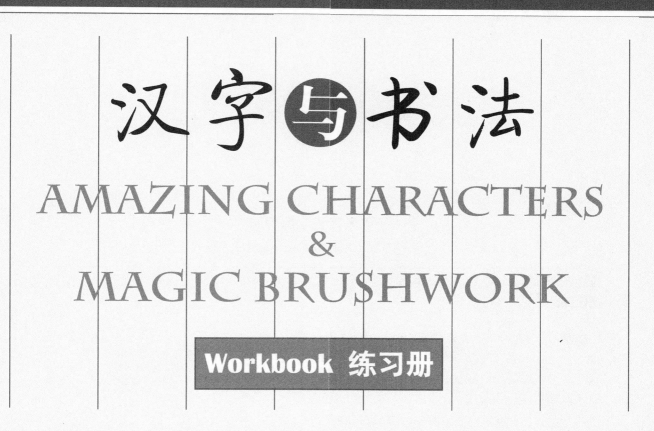

汉字与书法

AMAZING CHARACTERS
&
MAGIC BRUSHWORK

Workbook 练习册

王晓钧　编著

By Xiaojun Wang

北京语言大学出版社
BEIJING LANGUAGE AND CULTURE
UNIVERSITY PRESS

图书在版编目（CIP）数据

汉字与书法．练习册 / 王晓钧编著 .－－ 北京：北京语言
大学出版社，2009.11（2018.11重印）
ISBN 978-7-5619-2533-1

Ⅰ.①汉… Ⅱ.①王… Ⅲ.①汉字－书法－对外汉语教学－教
学参考资料 Ⅳ.① J292.1

中国版本图书馆 CIP 数据核字（2009）第 214378 号

汉字与书法·练习册
HANZI YU SHUFA · LIANXICE

排版制作：北京创艺涵文化发展有限公司
责任印制：周 燚

出版发行：北京语言大学出版社
社　　址：北京市海淀区学院路 15 号，100083
网　　址：www.blcup.com
电子信箱：service@blcup.com
电　　话：编辑部　　82303650/3591/3648
　　　　　发行部　　82303647
　　　　　北语书店　82303653
　　　　　网购咨询　82303908
印　　刷：北京九州迅驰传媒文化有限公司
版　　次：2009 年 12 月第 1 版　　印　　次：2018 年 11 月第 4 次印刷
开　　本：889 毫米 × 1194 毫米 1/16　　印　　张：12
字　　数：44 千字
定　　价：58.00 元（含课本、练习册）

PRINTED IN CHINA

目　录
Contents

第一部分　硬笔书法练习

Section I　Hard-Tip Calligraphy

1

1 数　字
Numbers

1 Learn to write numbers in Chinese characters.

Number 数字	Meaning 字义	Pronunciation 发音	Character 汉字	Exercise 书写练习			
1	one	yī	一	一	一		
2	two	èr	二	二	二		
3	three	sān	三	三	三		
4	four	sì	四	四	四		
5	five	wǔ	五	五	五		
6	six	liù	六	六	六		
7	seven	qī	七	七	七		
8	eight	bā	八	八	八		
9	nine	jiǔ	九	九	九		
10	ten	shí	十	十	十		
100	hundred	bǎi	百	百	百		

（续表）

Number 数字	Meaning 字义	Pronunciation 发音	Character 汉字	Exercise 书写练习			
1,000	thousand	qiān	千/仟	千	仟		
10,000	ten thousand	wàn	万/萬	万	萬		
100,000	hundred thousand	shíwàn	十万	十	万		
1,000,000	million	bǎiwàn	百万	百	万		
10,000,000	ten million	qiānwàn	千万	千	万		
100,000,000	hundred million	yì	亿/億	亿	億		
0	zero	líng	零	零	零		

Trace and copy the following characters.

一	一							
二	二	二						
三	三	三						

四	丶	冂	四	四	四		
五	一	丁	五	五			
六	丶	亠	六	六			
七	一	七					
八	丿	八					
九	丿	九					
十	一	十					
百	一	亠	丆	百	百	百	
千	丿	千	千				
万	一	万	万				

萬	艹	卅	苗	萬	萬	萬	萬
亿	亻	亿					
億	亻	亻	伫	伫	伫	倍	倍
	億	億	億	億			
零	十	示	示	示	零	雺	雺
	零	零	零				

2 Match the following characters with the numbers.

(1) 九		207
(2) 十五		600,000,000
(3) 七十一		4,000,000
(4) 零		15
(5) 二百零七		100,800
(6) 三千八百九十五		0
(7) 十万零八百		9
(8) 四百万		71
(9) 六亿		90,000,000
(10) 九千万		3,895

3 Write Chinese characters for the following numbers.

(1) 5 _____   (2) 8 _____

(3) 10 _____   (4) 9 _____

(5) 7 _____   (6) 4 _____

(7) 30 _____   (8) 200 _____

(9) 1,000 _____   (10) 60,000 _____

(11) 9,000,000 _____   (12) 500,000,000 _____

(13) 120 _____   (14) 3,500 _____

(15) 60,700 _____

2 象形字
Pictographic Characters

Learn to write pictographic characters.

1）Group One: Characters relating to people and human body.

Meaning 字义	Pronunciation 发音	Character 汉字	Exercise 书写练习					
man; human being	rén	人	人	人				
female	nǔ	女	女	女				
son; child	zǐ	子	子	子				
heart	xīn	心	心	心				
hand	shǒu	手	手	手				
foot	zú	足	足	足				
ear	ěr	耳	耳	耳				
eye	mù	目	目	目				
mouth	kǒu	口	口	口				
face	miàn	面	面	面				

Trace and copy the following characters.

人	丿	人						
女	𡿨	女	女					
子	乛	了	子					
心	丶	心	心	心				
手	𠂉	手	手	手				
足	口	甲	早	足				
耳	一	丆	耳	耳				
目	冂	目	目					
口	冂	口						
面	一	丙	而	面	面			

（2）Group Two: Characters relating to nature.

Meaning 字义	Pronunciation 发音	Character 汉字	Exercise 书写练习				
sun	rì	日	日	日			
moon	yuè	月	月	月			
gold; metal	jīn	金	金	金			
water	shuǐ	水	水	水			
fire	huǒ	火	火	火			
rock; stone	shí	石	石	石			
mountain	shān	山	山	山			
rain	yǔ	雨	雨	雨			
electricity	diàn	电/電	电	電			
air	qì	气/氣	气	氣			

Trace and copy the following characters.

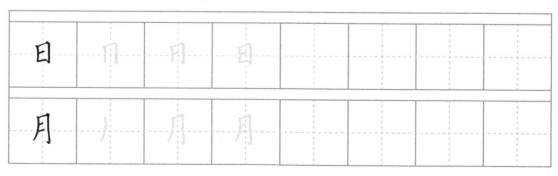

金	人	今	全	全	金	金	
水	亅	氺	水	水			
火	丶	火	火	火			
石	一	石	石	石			
山	丨	山	山				
雨	一	而	雨	雨	雨		
电	冂	申	申	电			
電	雷	電					
气	丿	气	气	气			
氣	氣	氣	氣	氣	氣		

（3）Group Three: Characters relating to animals.

Meaning 字义	Pronunciation 发音	Character 汉字	Exercise 书写练习				
cow	niú	牛	牛	牛			
horse	mǎ	马/馬	马	馬			
sheep	yáng	羊	羊	羊			
bird	niǎo	鸟/鳥	鸟	鳥			
fish	yú	鱼/魚	鱼	魚			
insect; worm	chóng	虫/蟲	虫	蟲			
shell	bèi	贝/貝	贝	貝			
hair; feather	máo	毛	毛	毛			
meat	ròu	肉	肉	肉			
horn	jiǎo	角	角	角			
skin; leather	pí	皮	皮	皮			

Trace and copy the following characters.

牛	丿	牜	牛				
马	马	马	马				
馬	一	二	馬	馬			
羊	丷	羊	羊				
鸟	鸟	鸟	鸟	鸟	鸟		
鳥	鸟	鸟	鳥	鳥	鳥		
鱼	夕	各	角	鱼	鱼		
虫	口	中	虫	虫			
蟲	虫	蚰	蟲				
贝	贝	贝					

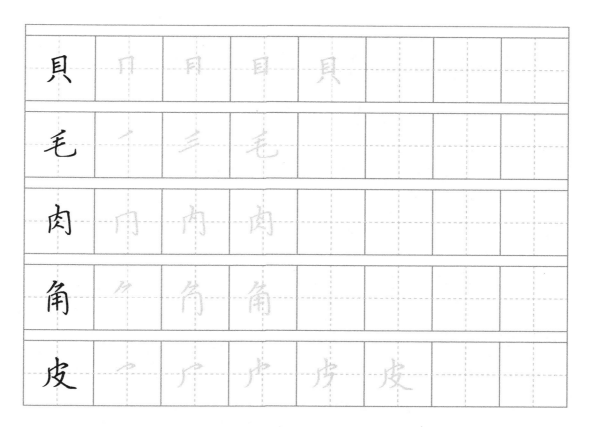

（4）Group Four: Characters relating to plants.

Meaning 字义	Pronunciation 发音	Character 汉字	Exercise 书写练习					
grass	cǎo	艸	艸	艸				
wood	mù	木	木	木				
bamboo	zhú	竹	竹	竹				
rice	mǐ	米	米	米				
melon	guā	瓜	瓜	瓜				
fruit	guǒ	果	果	果				

（续表）

Meaning 字义	Pronunciation 发音	Character 汉字	Exercise 书写练习					
rice plant; millet	hé	禾	禾	禾				
thread	sī	丝/絲	丝	絲				
field; farmland	tián	田	田	田				
soil	tǔ	土	土	土				
farm tool	lěi	耒	耒	耒				

Trace and copy the following characters.

艸	匸	匸	屮	如	艸	艸	
木	十	十	木				
竹	⺦	⺦	竹	竹			
米	丷	半	半	米			
瓜	厂	厂	瓜	瓜	瓜		

果	日	旦	旱	畢	果			
禾	丿		禾					
丝	ㄥ	幺	幺幺	丝				
絲	幺	幺	糸	絆	絲			
田	冂	门	冊	田				
土	一	十	土					
耒	三	丰	耒					

（5）Group Five: Characters relating to tools.

Meaning 字义	Pronunciation 发音	Character 汉字	Exercise 书写练习				
work; tool	gōng	工	工	工			
measure word	dǒu	斗	斗	斗			
knife	dāo	刀	刀	刀			
spoon	sháo	勺	勺	勺			
bow	gōng	弓	弓	弓			
dagger	gē	戈	戈	戈			
boat	zhōu	舟	舟	舟			
vehicle	chē	车/車	车	車			
door	mén	门/門	门	門			
well	jǐng	井	井	井			
net	wǎng	网/網	网	網			

Trace and copy the following characters.

工	一	丁	工				
斗	丶	斗	斗				
刀	刀	刀					
勺	勹	勺	勺				
弓	弓	弓	弓				
戈	一	弋	戈	戈			
舟	舟	舟	舟	舟			
车	一	丰	车	车			
車	一	車	車	車			
门	丶	门	门				

門	﹁	㇆	門	門	門	門	
井	二	井	井				
网	冂	冈	网				
網	糹	紵	紵	網	網	網	

3 指事字
Indicative Characters

Learn to write indicative characters.

Meaning 字义	Pronunciation 发音	Character 汉字	Exercise 书写练习					
above	shàng	上	上	上				
below	xià	下	下	下				
blade	rèn	刃	刃	刃				
root	běn	本	本	本				
end; tip	mò	末	末	末				
door bolt	shuān	闩/閂	闩	閂				
fork	chā	叉	叉	叉				
sky	tiān	天	天	天				
dawn	dàn	旦	旦	旦				
excessive; over	tài	太	太	太				
Chinese inch	cùn	寸	寸	寸				

Trace and copy the following characters.

上	丨	卜	上				
下	一	丅	下				
刃	フ	刀	刃				
本	一	十	木	本			
末	二	十	末				
闩	闩	闩					
門	門	門					
叉	フ	叉	叉				
天	二	三	天				
旦	旦	旦					

太　一　大　太

寸　一　十　寸

4 会意字
Suggestive Characters

Learn to write suggestive characters.

Meaning 字义	Pronunciation 发音	Character 汉字	Exercise 书写练习				
good	hǎo	好	好	好			
male; man	nán	男	男	男			
follow	cóng	从/從	从	從			
tenant-peasant	diàn	佃	佃	佃			
rest	xiū	休	休	休			
sleep	shuì	睡	睡	睡			
ask	wèn	问/問	问	問			
not busy; idle	xián	闲/閑	闲	閑			
hear	wén	闻/聞	闻	聞			
country	guó	国/國	国	國			
woods	lín	林	林	林			

（续表）

Meaning 字义	Pronunciation 发音	Character 汉字	Exercise 书写练习					
forest	sēn	森	森	森				
seedling	miáo	苗	苗	苗				
bright	míng	明	明	明				
between; space	jiān	间/間	间	間				
time	shí	时/時	时	時				
autumn	qiū	秋	秋	秋				
thunder	léi	雷	雷	雷				
pair; both	shuāng	双/雙	双	雙				
divide	fēn	分	分	分				

Trace and copy the following characters.

好	女	好					
男	田	男					

从	人	从					
從	彳	彴	祌	祌	從	從	
佃	亻	佃					
休	亻	休					
睡	目	盽	盰	盰	睡	睡	
问	门	问					
問	門	門	問				
闲	门	闲					
閒	門	門	閒				
闻	门	闰	闻	闻			

聞	門	聞					
国	门	国	国	国			
國	冂	冃	同	囼	國	國	國
林	十	林					
森	木	森	森				
苗	一	艹	艹	苗			
明	日	明					
间	门	间					
間	門	間					
时	日	时					

時	吐	時					
秋	禾	秋					
雷	雷	雷					
双	又	双					
雙	雔	雔	雙				
分	八	分					

形声字
Pictophonetic Compounds

Learn to write pictophonetic compounds.

Meaning 字义	Pronunciation 发音	Character 汉字	Exercise 书写练习				
mother	mā	妈/媽	妈	媽			
milk; grandma	nǎi	奶	奶	奶			
river	hé	河	河	河			
machine	jī	机/機	机	機			
partner	huǒ	伙	伙	伙			
think; want to	xiǎng	想	想	想			
gun	qiāng	枪/槍	枪	槍			
bell; clock	zhōng	钟/鐘	钟	鐘			
sample; appearance	yàng	样/樣	样	樣			
vegetable; dish	cài	菜	菜	菜			
grass	cǎo	草	草	草			

（续表）

Meaning 字义	Pronunciation 发音	Character 汉字	Exercise 书写练习			
property	cái	财/財	财	財		
hungry	è	饿/餓	饿	餓		
be full	bǎo	饱/飽	饱	飽		
slow	màn	慢	慢	慢		
busy	máng	忙	忙	忙		
school	xiào	校	校	校		
laugh; smile	xiào	笑	笑	笑		
city; city wall	chéng	城	城	城		
village	cūn	村	村	村		

Trace and copy the following characters.

妈	女	妈					
媽	女	媽					

奶	女	奶	奶				
河	氵	汁	沪	汈	河		
机	木	机					
機	木	棤	棬	機	機	機	
伙	亻	伙					
想	木	相	想				
枪	木	抢	枪				
槍	木	枪	棆	槍			
样	木	样					
樣	木	样	樣				

菜	艹	芧	菜					
草	艹	苩	草					
财	贝	财						
財	貝	財						
饿	饣	饿						
餓	食	餓						
饱	饣	饱						
飽	食	飽						
慢	忄	悍	慢					
忙	忄	忙						

校	木	校						
笑	灬	笑						
城	土	城						
村	木	村						

6 不同书体练习
Writing in Different Styles

发音与字义 Pronun-ciation & Meaning	甲骨文 Bone and Shell Script	金文 Bronze Script	小篆 The Small Seal Style	隶书 The Clerical Style	楷书 The Regular Style	行书 The Running Style	草书 The Grass Style
man rén	几	入	尺	人	人	人	亾

发音与字义 Pronunciation & Meaning	甲骨文 Bone and Shell Script	金文 Bronze Script	小篆 The Small Seal Style	隶书 The Clerical Style	楷书 The Regular Style	行书 The Running Style	草书 The Grass Style
baby zǐ	子	子	子	子	子	子	子
famle nǚ	女	女	女	女	女	女	女

发音与字义 Pronun-ciation & Mean-ing	甲骨文 Bone and Shell Script	金文 Bronze Script	小篆 The Small Seal Style	隶书 The Clerical Style	楷书 The Regular Style	行书 The Running Style	草书 The Grass Style
heart xīn							
mountain shān							

发音与字义 Pronunciation & Meaning	甲骨文 Bone and Shell Script	金文 Bronze Script	小篆 The Small Seal Style	隶书 The Clerical Style	楷书 The Regular Style	行书 The Running Style	草书 The Grass Style
water shuǐ	水	水	水	水	水	水	水
moon yuè	D	D	月	月	月	月	月

发音与字义 Pronunciation & Meaning	甲骨文 Bone and Shell Script	金文 Bronze Script	小篆 The Small Seal Style	隶书 The Clerical Style	楷书 The Regular Style	行书 The Running Style	草书 The Grass Style
wood mù	木	木	木	木	木	木	木
rain yǔ	雨	雨	雨	雨	雨	雨	雨

发音与字义 Pronunciation & Meaning	甲骨文 Bone and Shell Script	金文 Bronze Script	小篆 The Small Seal Style	隶书 The Clerical Style	楷书 The Regular Style	行书 The Running Style	草书 The Grass Style
ox niú							
sheep yáng							

发音与字义 Pronunciation & Meaning	甲骨文 Bone and Shell Script	金文 Bronze Script	小篆 The Small Seal Style	隶书 The Clerical Style	楷书 The Regular Style	行书 The Running Style	草书 The Grass Style
horse mǎ							
fish yú							

发音与字义 Pronun-ciation & Mean-ing	甲骨文 Bone and Shell Script	金文 Bronze Script	小篆 The Small Seal Style	隶书 The Clerical Style	楷书 The Regular Style	行书 The Running Style	草书 The Grass Style
door mén	門	門	門	门	门	门	门
well jǐng	井	井	井	井	井	井	井

发音与字义 Pronun- ciation & Mean- ing	甲骨文 Bone and Shell Script	金文 Bronze Script	小篆 The Small Seal Style	隶书 The Clerical Style	楷书 The Regular Style	行书 The Running Style	草书 The Grass Style
net wǎng	网	网	网	网	网	网	网
cart/ vehicle chē	車	車	車	车	车	车	车

第二部分　毛笔书法练习

Section II　　Calligraphy by Brush　**2**

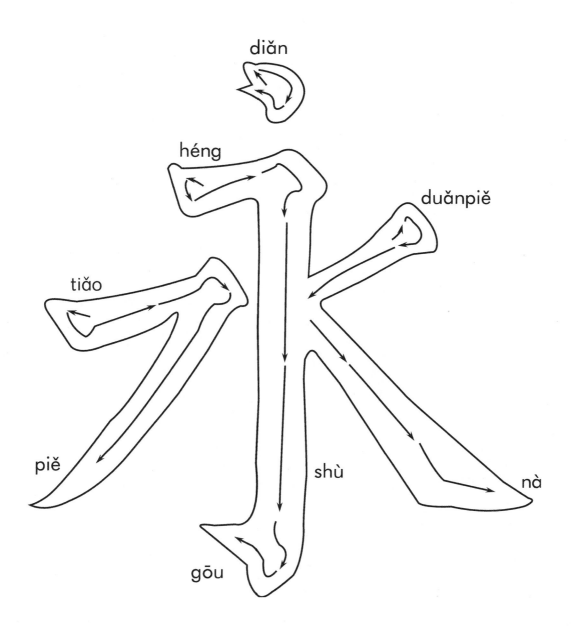

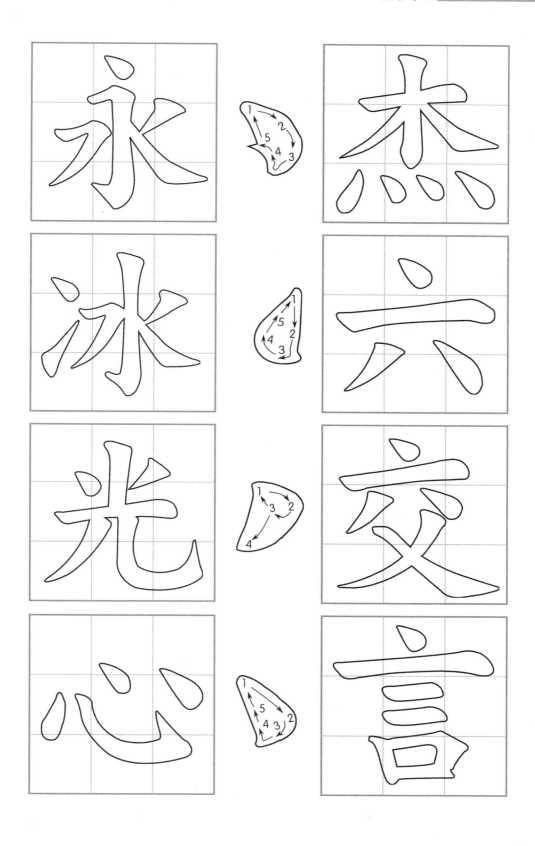

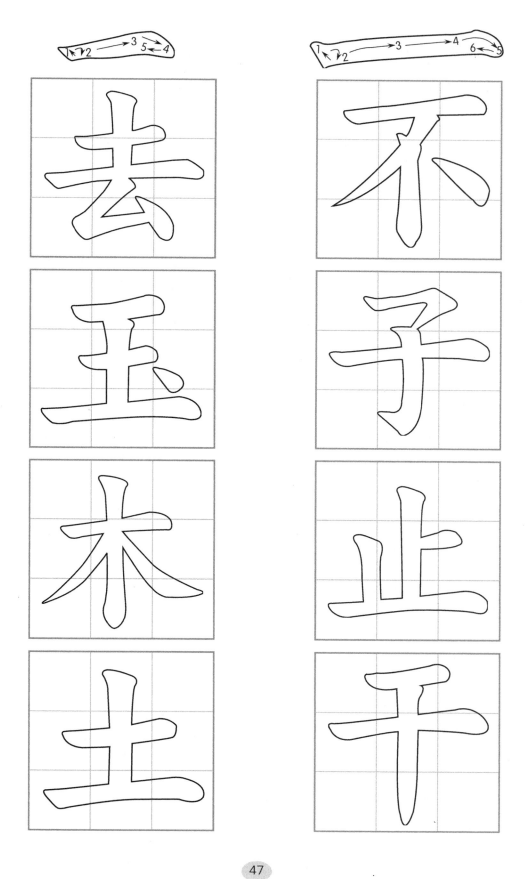

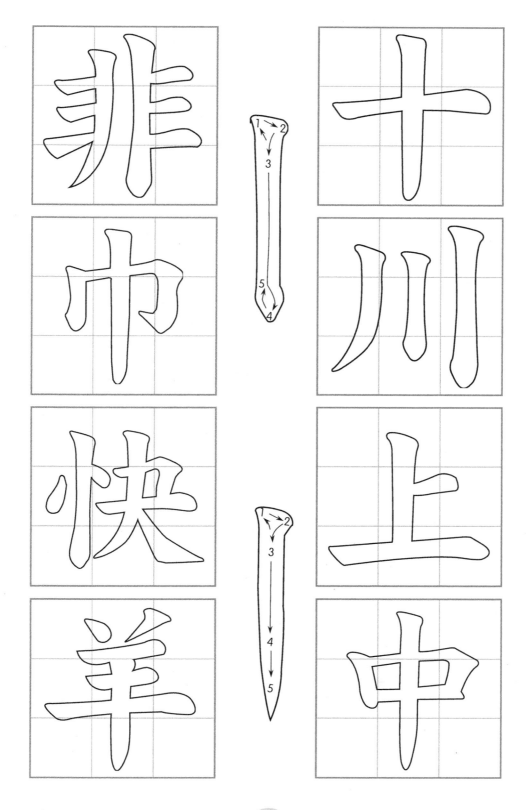

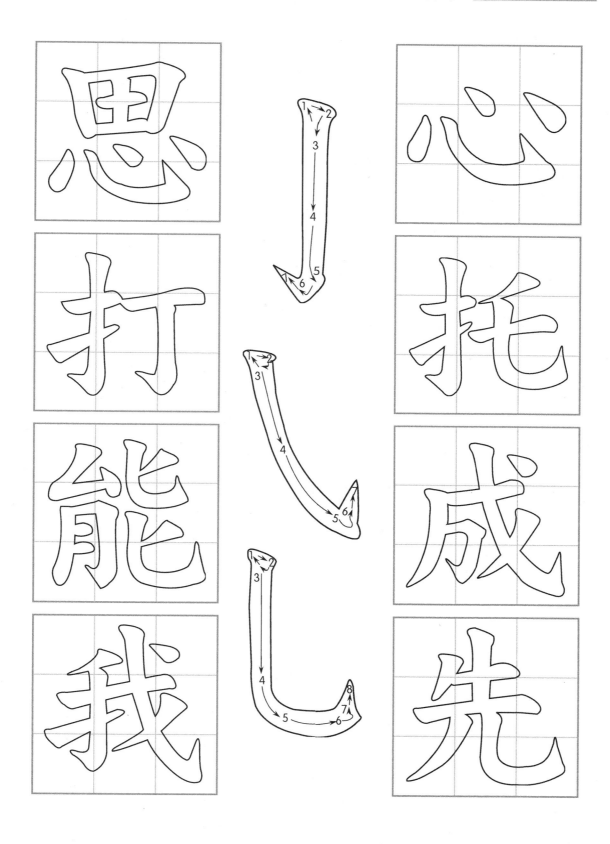

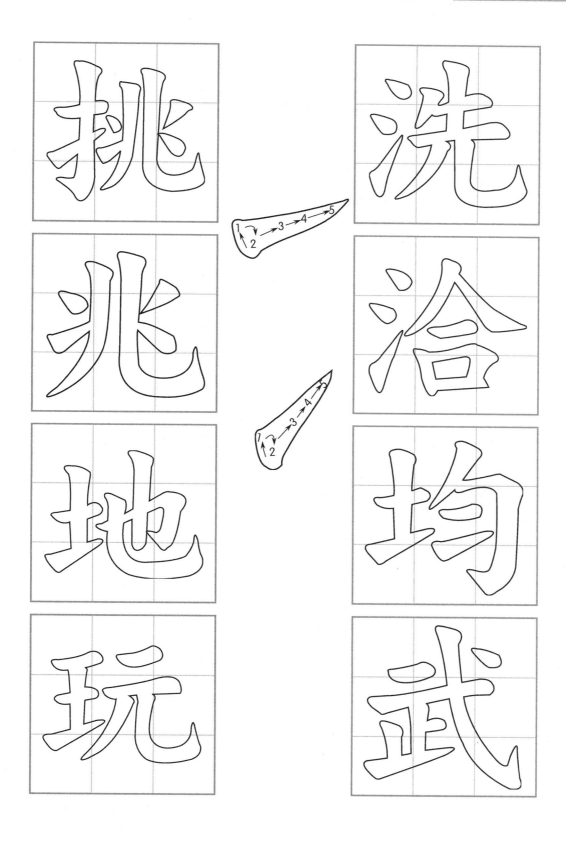

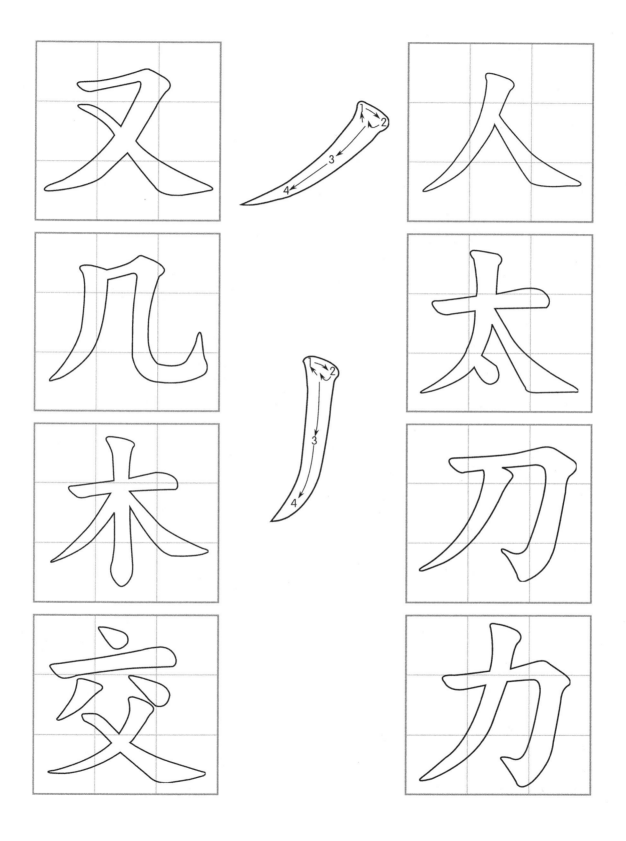

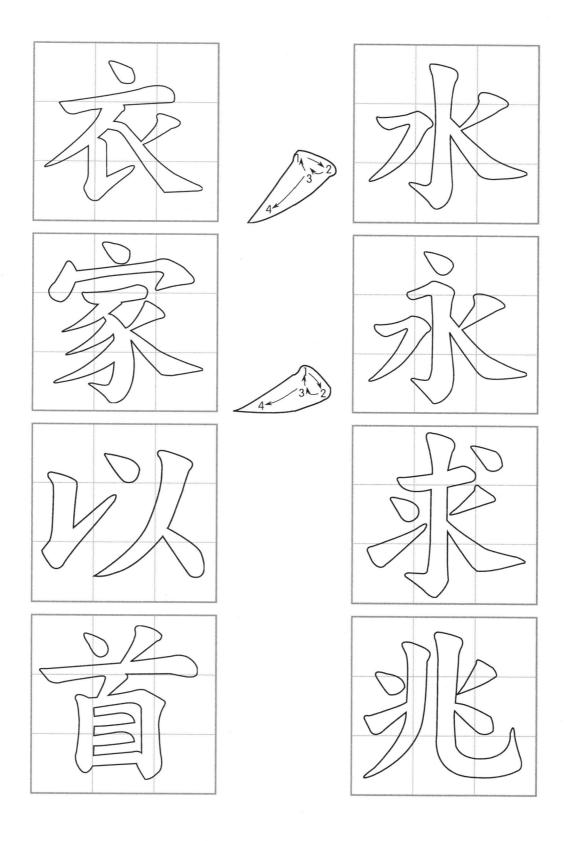

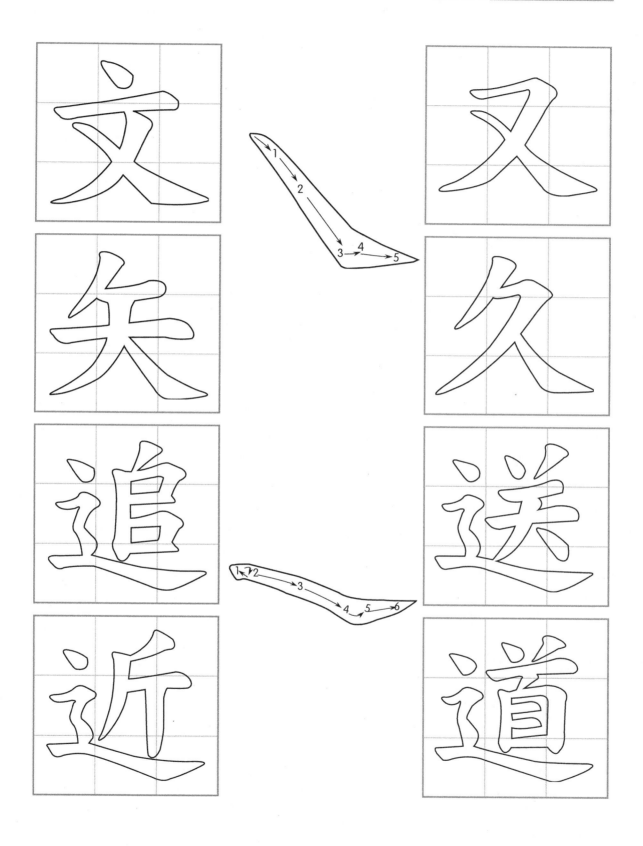

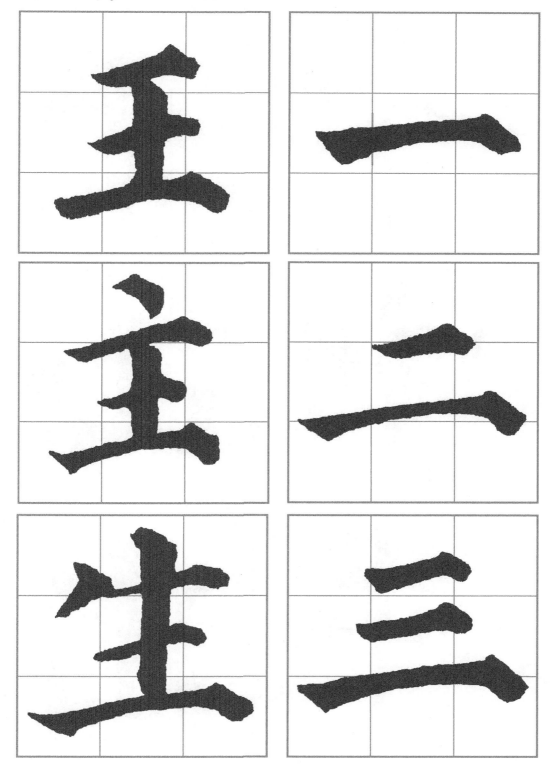

2 临帖练习
Copy the Model Works

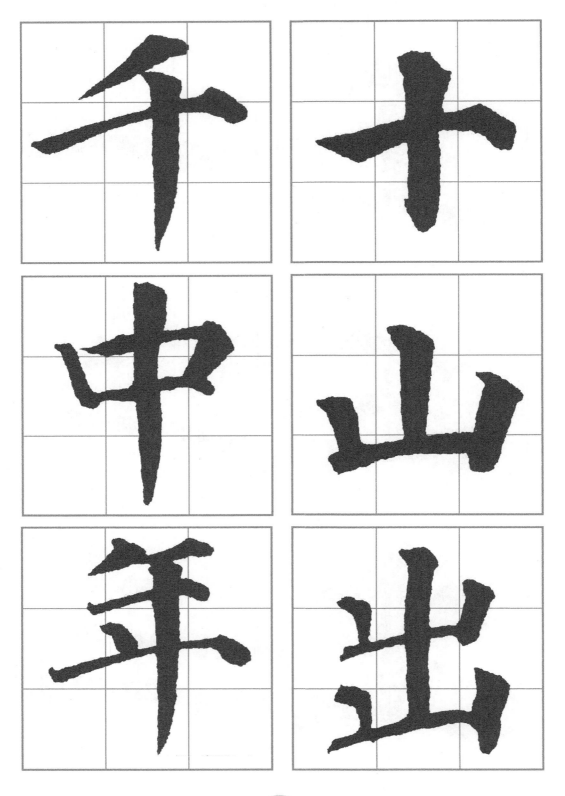

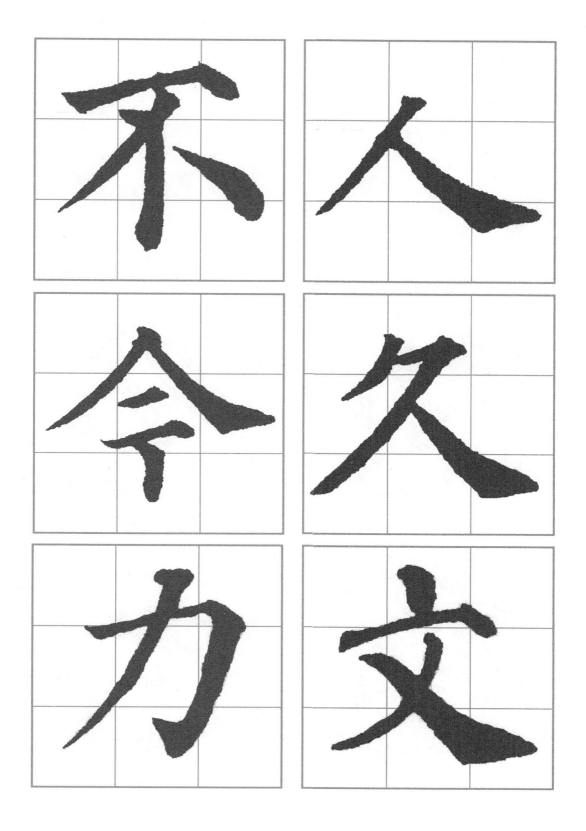

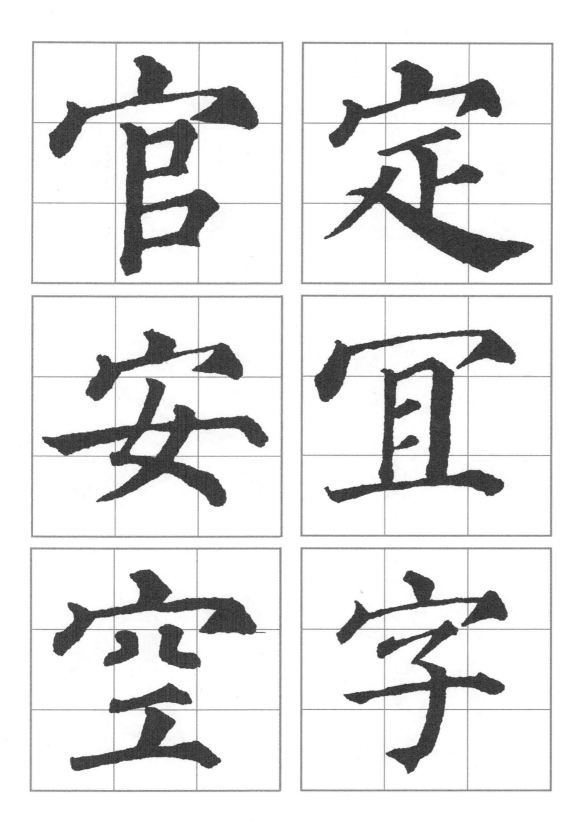

师从书法四大家
Follow the Four Famous Calligraphers

Yan Style （颜体）

部	生	宇
都	至	宗
勃	並	空
動	直	宣

Liu Style （柳体）

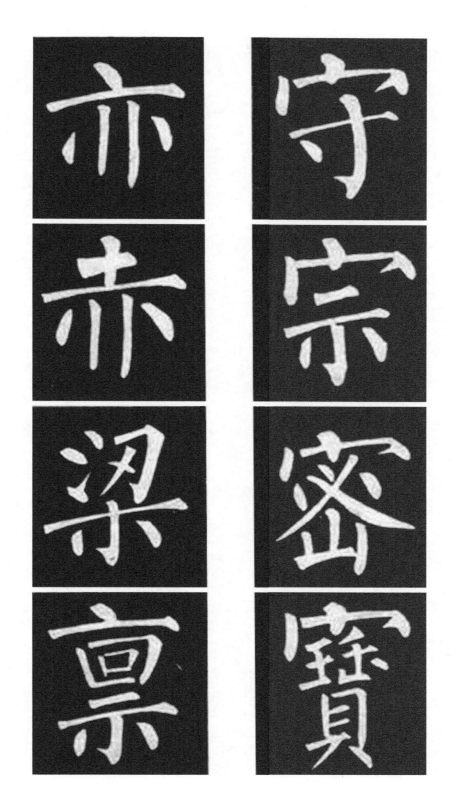

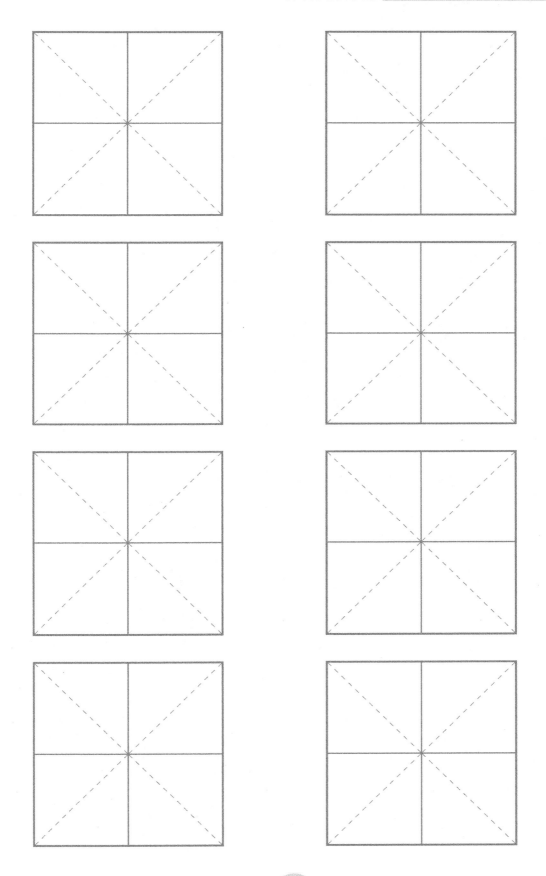

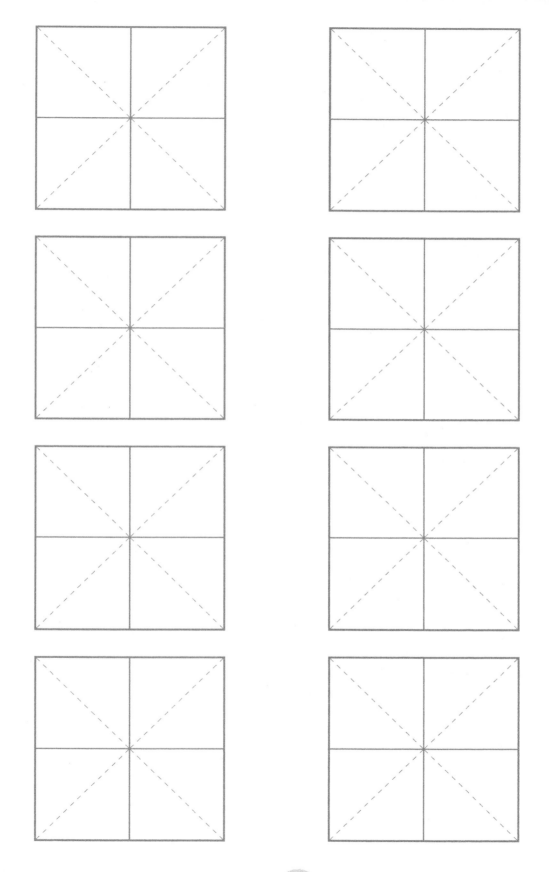

Ou Style （欧体）

此	南	右
奄	帝	宫
流	带	泉
深	奉	当

Zhao Style （赵体）

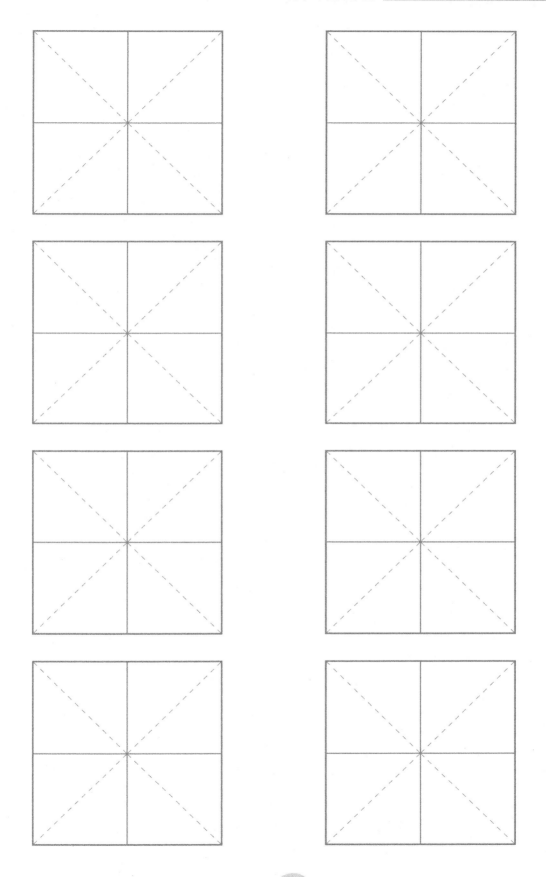

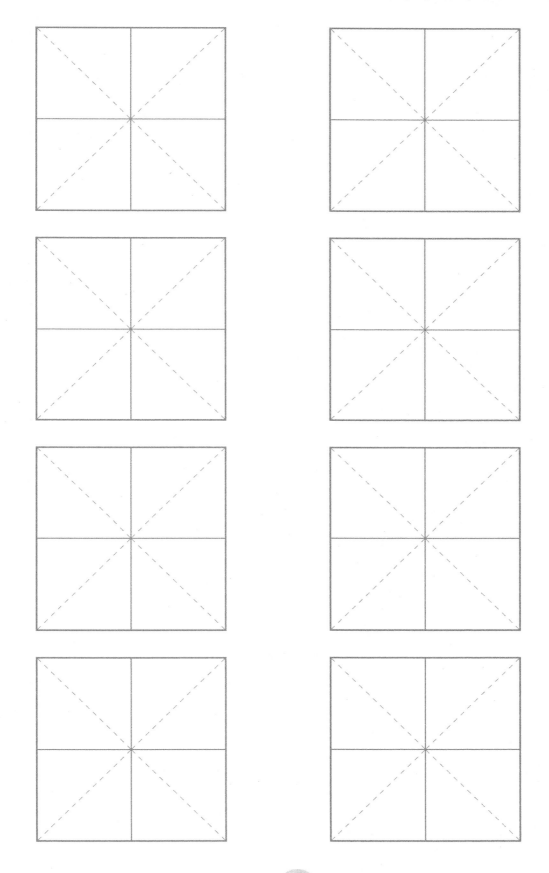

4 脱帖练习
Freehand Practice

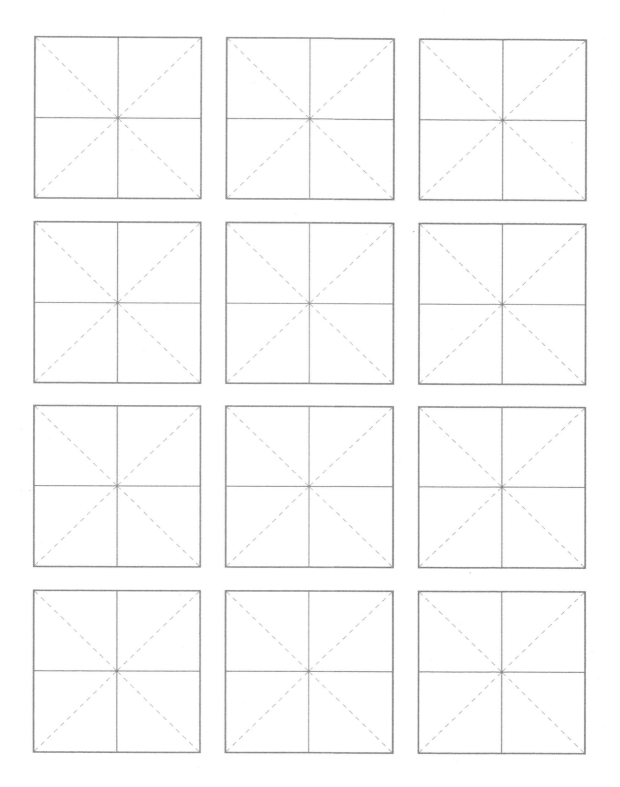

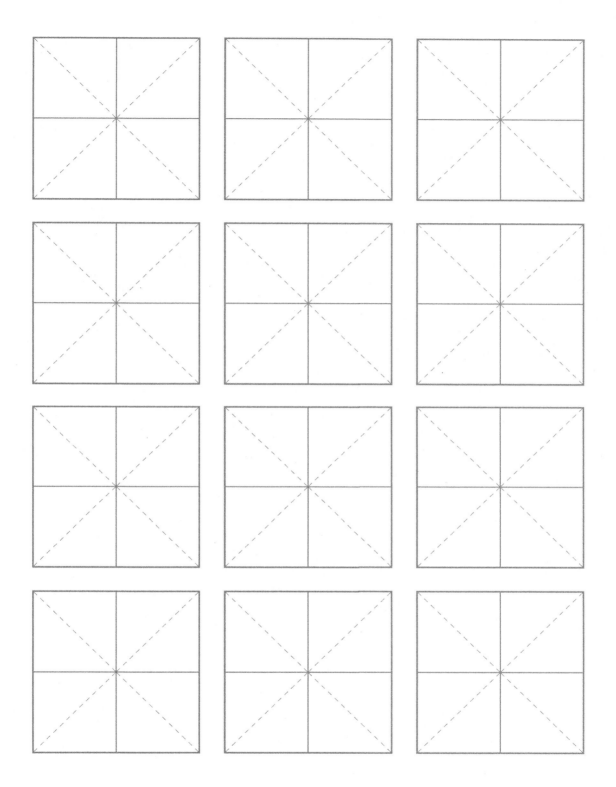

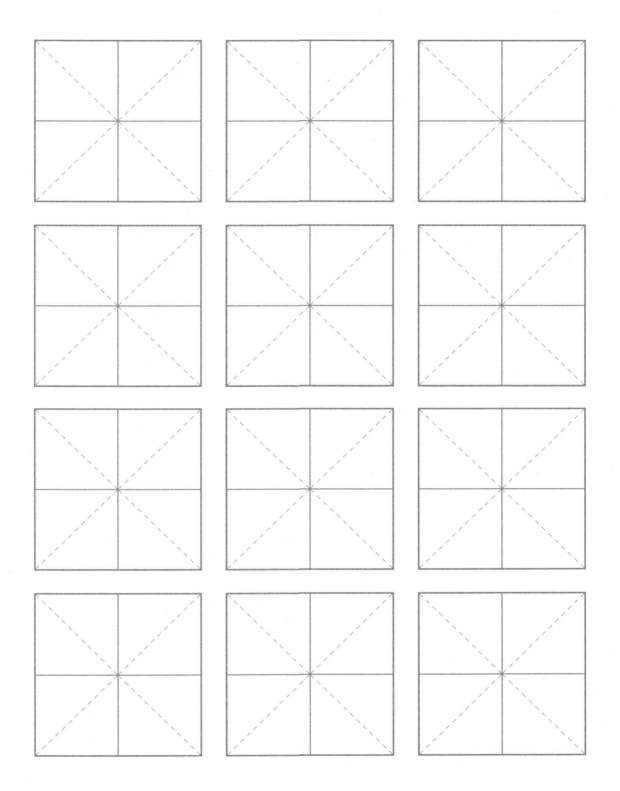

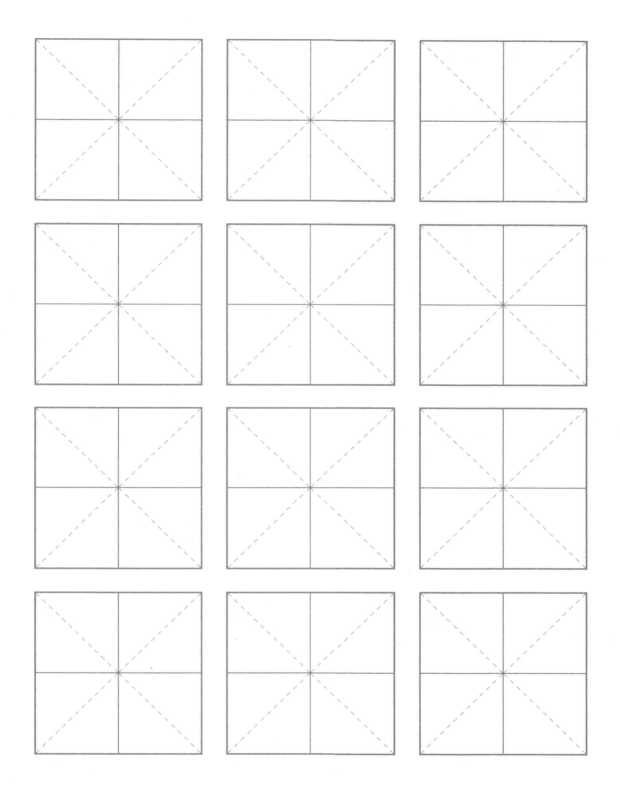

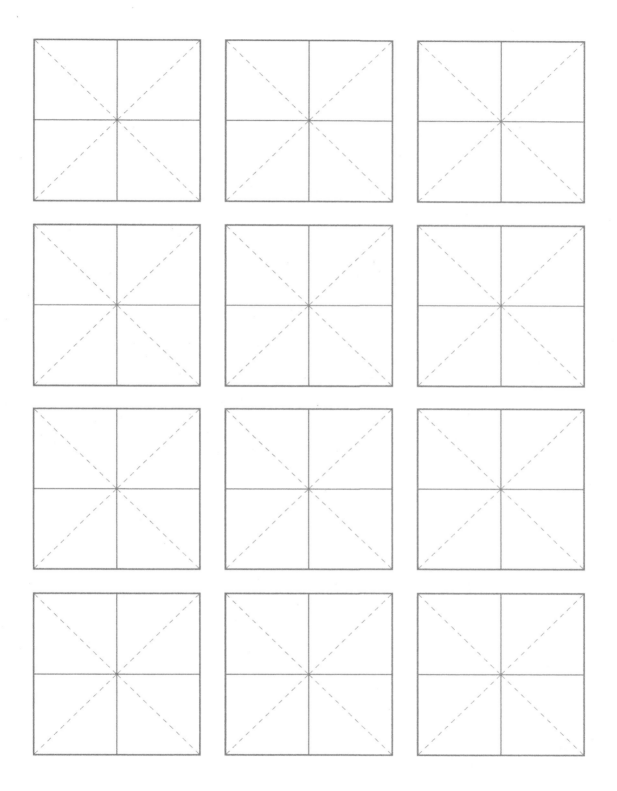

附　录
Appendices

常用汉字
Most Commonly Used Characters

(共795个字[1] Total: 795 characters)

啊	矮	爱	安	八	把	爸	吧
白	百	摆	班	搬	般	板	半
办	帮	包	保	抱	报	杯	北
被	备	本	比	笔	必	毕	币
边	变	遍	便	表	别	病	播
不	部	步	擦	才	彩	菜	参
操	草	厕	层	叉	茶	查	差
产	常	长	场	厂	唱	朝	车

[1] 参见国家对外汉语教学领导小组办公室编写的《高等学校外国留学生汉语言专业教学大纲（附件一）》，北京语言大学出版社，2002年。

晨	衬	城	成	吃	迟	持	抽
出	除	楚	础	穿	船	窗	床
吹	春	磁	词	次	从	村	错
答	打	大	戴	带	代	单	但
蛋	当	刀	倒	导	到	道	得
的	灯	等	低	地	第	弟	点
典	电	店	调	掉	定	丢	东
冬	懂	动	都	读	度	短	段
锻	对	顿	多	饿	而	儿	二
发	法	翻	烦	反	饭	方	房

访	放	非	飞	啡	分	丰	封
风	夫	服	福	辅	府	复	负
父	傅	附	富	该	改	概	干
感	敢	刚	钢	高	搞	告	哥
歌	个	各	给	根	跟	更	工
公	共	够	姑	故	顾	刮	挂
关	观	馆	惯	广	贵	国	果
过	哈	还	孩	海	寒	喊	汉
航	好	号	喝	和	合	河	何
黑	很	红	后	候	忽	湖	互

户	花	画	化	话	划	坏	欢
换	黄	回	会	活	火	或	机
基	鸡	极	级	集	急	挤	几
己	技	寄	计	记	纪	绩	继
济	家	加	假	架	驾	坚	间
检	简	见	件	健	将	江	讲
交	教	蕉	脚	角	饺	叫	较
接	街	节	结	解	姐	借	介
界	斤	今	紧	进	近	精	睛
经	静	净	究	久	九	酒	旧

就	桔	局	举	句	卷	决	觉
咖	卡	开	看	康	考	棵	科
咳	可	渴	克	刻	客	课	空
口	哭	苦	裤	快	块	筷	况
困	拉	啦	来	蓝	篮	览	劳
老	了	累	冷	离	里	理	礼
立	例	历	力	俩	联	连	脸
练	炼	凉	两	辆	亮	谅	聊
零	留	流	六	楼	路	录	旅
绿	乱	论	妈	麻	马	码	吗

买	卖	满	慢	忙	毛	冒	帽
么	没	每	妹	门	们	米	面
民	名	明	母	目	拿	哪	那
奶	南	男	难	闹	呢	内	能
你	年	念	娘	您	牛	农	努
女	暖	爬	怕	拍	排	派	盘
旁	胖	跑	朋	碰	批	啤	篇
片	漂	票	苹	平	评	瓶	破
七	期	骑	齐	起	汽	气	器
铅	千	钱	前	浅	墙	桥	且

切	亲	青	轻	清	晴	情	请
秋	求	球	取	去	全	确	然
让	热	人	任	认	日	容	肉
如	赛	三	散	色	山	商	上
烧	勺	少	绍	舍	身	深	什
生	声	省	剩	师	十	时	食
识	拾	史	始	世	室	事	是
市	试	示	视	适	收	手	首
输	书	舒	熟	数	树	术	束
双	谁	水	睡	说	司	思	死

四	送	嗽	宿	诉	算	虽	岁
所	他	她	它	拾	太	态	谈
汤	糖	堂	躺	讨	特	疼	踢
提	题	体	天	条	跳	铁	听
停	庭	挺	通	同	痛	头	突
图	推	腿	退	脱	袜	外	完
玩	碗	晚	万	往	网	望	忘
危	围	为	喂	位	文	闻	问
我	握	屋	五	午	舞	物	误
务	西	希	息	习	喜	洗	系

细	下	夏	先	险	现	相	香
箱	想	响	像	向	消	小	笑
校	些	鞋	写	谢	辛	新	心
信	星	行	幸	姓	兴	休	需
须	许	续	学	雪	呀	研	言
颜	眼	演	宴	验	羊	阳	扬
样	要	药	也	夜	业	页	一
医	衣	宜	椅	已	以	艺	亿
意	易	谊	译	因	音	阴	银
英	应	赢	迎	影	永	泳	用

邮	游	有	友	右	又	鱼	愉
雨	语	遇	预	寓	育	元	原
圆	员	园	远	愿	院	月	乐
云	运	杂	再	在	咱	脏	澡
早	责	怎	增	展	占	站	张
章	着	找	照	者	这	真	整
正	政	只	织	支	知	之	直
指	纸	治	志	中	钟	种	重
周	猪	主	住	注	祝	助	装
准	桌	自	字	子	总	走	租

足	族	组	嘴	最	昨	左	做
作	坐	座					

2 中文组字部件
Chinese Components

No.	Radical	Variant(s)	*Pinyin*	English Meaning	Stroke Count
1	一		yī	one	1
2	丨		gǔn	the vertical	1
3	丿		piě	the left falling	1
4	丶		zhǔ	the dot	1
5	⺄	乛、乁、乚、乙	zhé	the horizontal turning	1
6	十		shí	ten	2
7	厂	厂	hàn	cliff	2
8	匚		fāng	square box	2
9	卜	⼘	bǔ	divining	2
10	冂	冂	jiōng	wilderness	2
11	八	丷	bā	eight; part, divide	2
12	人	亻、入	rén	man	2
13	勹		bāo	wrap	2
14	儿		ér	son	2
15	匕		bǐ	spoon, dagger	2
16	几	几	jī	small table	2
17	亠		tóu	head; above	2
18	冫		bīng	ice	2
19	冖		mì	cover	2
20	凵		qiǎn	wide opened mouth	2
21	卩	㔾	jié	seal	2

（续表）

No.	Radical	Variant(s)	*Pinyin*	English Meaning	Stroke Count
22	刀	刂、⺈	dāo	knife	2
23	力		lì	power	2
24	又		yòu	again	2
25	厶		sī	private	2
26	廴		yǐn	walk a long distance	2
27	干		gān	shield	3
28	工		gōng	work	3
29	土	士	tǔ	earth	3
30	艹	艸	ǎo	grass	3
31	寸		cùn	1/30 meter	3
32	廾		gǒng	two hands	3
33	大		dà	big	3
34	尢	兀、尣	wāng	lame	3
35	弋		yì	shoot	3
36	小	⺌	xiǎo	small	3
37	口		kǒu	mouth	3
38	囗		wéi	enclosure	3
39	山		shān	mountain	3
40	巾		jīn	towel	3
41	彳		chì	walk slowly	3
42	彡		shān	hair, feather	3
43	夕		xī	evening	3
44	夂		suī	walk slowly	3

（续表）

No.	Radical	Variant(s)	*Pinyin*	English Meaning	Stroke Count
45	丬	爿	pán	half tree trunk	3
46	广		yǎn	house built at a slope	3
47	门	門	mén	gate	3
48	宀		mián	roof	3
49	辶	辵	chuò	walk	3
50	彐	彐、彑	jì	pig's head	3
51	尸		shī	corpse	3
52	己	已、巳	jǐ	oneself	3
53	弓		gōng	bow	3
54	子		zǐ	child	3
55	屮	㞢	chè	sprout	3
56	女		nǔ	woman	3
57	飞	飛	fēi	fly	3
58	马	馬	mǎ	horse	3
59	幺		yāo	small, young	3
60	巛		chuān	river	3
61	王	玉	wáng	king	4
62	无	旡	wú	not	4
63	韦	韋	wéi	tanned leather	4
64	木	朩	mù	tree, wood	4
65	支		zhī	branch	4
66	犬	犭	quǎn	dog	4
67	歹	歺	dǎi	evil	4

（续表）

No.	Radical	Variant(s)	*Pinyin*	English Meaning	Stroke Count
68	车、车	車	chē	cart	4
69	牙		yá	tooth	4
70	戈		gē	dagger	4
71	比		bǐ	side by side; compare	4
72	瓦		wǎ	tile	4
73	止		zhǐ	stop	4
74	攴	攵	pū	whip	4
75	日、曰	⊟	rì、yuē	sun	4
76	贝	貝	bèi	shell	4
77	水	氵、氺	shuǐ	water	4
78	见	見	jiàn	see	4
79	牛、牜	⺧	niú	cow, ox	4
80	手	扌、龵	shǒu	hand	4
81	气		qì	air, breath	4
82	毛		máo	fur	4
83	长	镸、長	cháng	long	4
84	片		piàn	slice	4
85	斤		jīn	axe	4
86	爪	爫	zhǎo	claw	4
87	父		fù	father	4
88	月	月	yuè	moon	4
89	氏		shì	clan	4
90	欠		qiàn	yawn; lack	4

（续表）

No.	Radical	Variant(s)	*Pinyin*	English Meaning	Stroke Count
91	风	風	fēng	wind	4
92	殳		shū	weapon	4
93	文		wén	script	4
94	方		fāng	square	4
95	火	灬	huǒ	fire	4
96	斗		dǒu	dipper	4
97	户		hù	door	4
98	心	忄、⺗	xīn	heart	4
99	毋	母	wú	do not	4
100	示	礻	shì	worship or ceremony	5
101	甘		gān	sweet	5
102	石		shí	stone	5
103	龙	龍	lóng	dragon	5
104	业		yè	business	5
105	目		mù	eye	5
106	田		tián	field	5
107	罒		wǎng	net	5
108	皿		mǐn	utensil	5
109	生		shēng	give birth	5
110	矢		shǐ	arrow	5
111	禾		hé	grain	5
112	白		bái	white	5
113	瓜		guā	melon	5

（续表）

No.	Radical	Variant(s)	*Pinyin*	English Meaning	Stroke Count
114	鸟	鳥	niǎo	bird	5
115	疒		nè	sickness	5
116	立		lì	stand	5
117	穴		xué	cave	5
118	疋	⺪	pǐ	*a measure word for bolts of cloth*	5
119	皮		pí	skin	5
120	癶		bō	a person stands with his feet seperated	5
121	矛		máo	spear	5
122	耒		lěi	plow	6
123	老	耂	lǎo	old	6
124	耳		ěr	ear	6
125	臣		chén	minister	6
126	覀、西		xī	west	6
127	而		ér	bristles on the jaws; and	6
128	页	頁	yè	page	6
129	至		zhì	arrive	6
130	虍	虎	hǔ	tiger	6
131	虫		chóng	insect	6
132	肉		ròu	meat	6
133	缶		fǒu	jar	6
134	舌		shé	tongue	6
135	竹、⺮		zhú	bamboo	6
136	臼	𦥑	jiù	mortar	6

（续表）

No.	Radical	Variant(s)	*Pinyin*	English Meaning	Stroke Count
137	自		zì	self	6
138	血		xuè	blood	6
139	舟		zhōu	boat	6
140	色		sè	color	6
141	齐	齊	qí	even	6
142	衣	衤	yī	clothes	6
143	羊	羌、𦍌	yáng	sheep	6
144	米		mǐ	rice	6
145	聿	肀、𦘒、畫	yù	brush	6
146	艮	𭥫	gèn	stop	6
147	羽		yǔ	feather	6
148	糸	纟、糹	mì	silk	6
149	麦	麥	mài	wheat	7
150	走		zǒu	run	7
151	赤		chì	red	7
152	豆		dòu	bean	7
153	酉		yǒu	wine	7
154	辰		chén	morning	7
155	豕		shǐ	pig	7
156	卤	鹵	lǔ	salt	7
157	里		lǐ	alley, lane; village	7
158	足	⻊	zú	foot	7
159	邑	阝 (right)	yì	city	7

No.	Radical	Variant(s)	*Pinyin*	English Meaning	Stroke Count
160	身		shēn	body	7
161	釆		biàn	distinguish	7
162	谷		gǔ	valley	7
163	豸		zhì	worm	7
164	龟	龜	guī	turtle	7
165	角		jiǎo	horn	7
166	言	讠	yán	speech	7
167	辛		xīn	hard	7
168	青		qīng	blue	8
169	卓	/	/	/	8
170	雨、⻗		yǔ	rain	8
171	非		fēi	wrong	8
172	齿	齒	chǐ	tooth	8
173	黾	黽	mǐn	frog	8
174	隹		zhuī	short-tailed bird	8
175	阜	阝 (left)	fù	mound	8
176	金	钅	jīn	gold	8
177	鱼	魚	yú	fish	8
178	隶		lì	slave	8
179	革		gé	leather	9
180	面		miàn	face	9
181	韭		jiǔ	leek	9
182	骨		gǔ	bone	9

（续表）

No.	Radical	Variant(s)	*Pinyin*	English Meaning	Stroke Count
183	香		xiāng	fragrant	9
184	鬼		guǐ	ghost	9
185	食	饣、飠	shí	eat	9
186	音		yīn	sound	9
187	首		shǒu	head	9
188	髟		biāo	hair	10
189	鬲		lì	cauldron	10
190	鬥		dòu	fight	10
191	高		gāo	tall	10
192	黃		huáng	yellow	11
193	麻		má	hemp	11
194	鹿		lù	deer	11
195	鼎		dǐng	tripod cauldron	12
196	黑		hēi	black	12
197	黍		shǔ	millet	12
198	鼓		gǔ	drum	13
199	鼠		shǔ	rat	13
200	鼻		bí	nose	14
201	龠		yuè	flute	17

3 问题解答
Answer Keys

1. 书法就是书写的艺术，也就是如何使书写艺术化或专业化。

2. 世界上至少有1000种以上的书写系统或书面语。根据书写符号的音、形、义之间的关系，基本上可以把这些书写系统分为三类：

   (1) 表音系统，比如英文和其他拉丁系语言所使用的字母。

   (2) 音节系统，比如日文使用的音节符号——假名。

   (3) 表意系统，比如中文使用的汉字和其他象形文字。

3. 中国书法的起源可以追溯到几千年以前。中国书法的发展反映了中国文明和文化的进程。

4. 中国书法发展的根源是大自然。不仅汉字的基本字形来源于自然，而且书法的基本规则也是依据自然之美。

5. 中国书法一直被认为是一种独特的、最主要的东方艺术。书法与绘画、诗歌一起构成了东方艺术瑰宝。

6. 学习中国书法不仅可以培养审美意识，而且有助于大脑的发育和健康，因为中国书法需要大脑的左右脑同时活动和配合，而且也需要集中精神，保持平和冷静。学习书法也可以帮助母语为非汉语的学生学习汉字，增加学习兴趣。

Chapter One

1. Calligraphy means "good" or "beautiful" writing, i.e. writing as an art.

2. There are basically three writing systems classified among over 1,000 kinds of known written languages in the world.

   (1) Phonetic system, such as alphabetic letters in English and other Romance languages;

   (2) Syllabic system, such as *kana* in Japanese;

   (3) Logographic system, such as Chinese characters and other hieroglyphs.

3. Chinese calligraphy can be traced back to several thousand years ago. Its development mirrors the history of Chinese civilization and culture.

4. The basic inspiration of Chinese calligraphy is nature. Not only are the basic character forms derived from nature, but also the principles of calligraphy are based on the beauty of the natural world.

5. Chinese calligraphy has been considered one of the major oriental arts along with painting and poetry.

6. Learning Chinese calligraphy can help the development of the brain since it requires the involvement of both sides of the brain as well as concentration and calmness. It can also help those whose native languages are not Chinese to learn characters.

1. 1899年在河南安阳小屯村出土的甲骨文是有关汉字的最早的考古发现。此处为商朝（公元前1600~公元前1046）都城遗址，当时称为"殷"。这些文字刻在龟甲兽骨上，至今已发掘出10万多片。

2. 王懿荣发现"龙骨"上有很多刀刻的痕迹，这些刀痕正是汉字早期的形式。

3. 甲骨文也叫"殷墟文字"，主要是殷人占卜的记录。

4. 在10多万片甲骨刻片中，大约有5000多个单字，目前能够辨认的大约有1800个。

5. 许慎是汉朝著名的文字学家。他认为汉字是由黄帝的史官仓颉创造的。有人甚至说仓颉有四只眼睛。实际上，汉字很可能是由大众创造的，而仓颉进行了整理加工。

6. 早期汉字的字形在公元前221年由秦始皇下令进行了规范统一。

7. 大型的字典中收入的汉字超过了10万个，而日常使用的大约为3000个。学习中文的外国学生需要掌握1000个左右最常用的汉字。

Chapter Two

1. The first archeological evidence of Chinese characters was in 1899 with the discovery of over 100,000 pieces of oracle bone inscriptions carved on tortoise shells and animal bones from Xiaotun Village, Anyang County of Henan Province (formerly Yin, the site of the capital of Shang Dynasty, 1600 B.C.~1046 B.C.) .

2. Wang Yirong found that there were many knife markings on the "dragon bones" and the markings were ancient forms of Chinese characters.

3. The main focus of bone and shell script, also called "Yin Ruins' characters", is divination.

4. Almost 5,000 characters are inscribed among the 100,000 pieces of tortoise shells, only 1,800 of which have been identified.

5. Xu Shen was a famous philologist from the Han Dynasty. He suggested that Cang Jie, an official historian of Emperor Huang, created characters. Cang Jie is said to have special talents and that he even had four eyes! In fact, it makes more sense that Cang Jie assembled characters created by the common people.

6. The ancient forms of Chinese characters were standardized in 221 B.C. by Emperor Qin Shihuang.

7. More than 100,000 characters were contained in the largest dictionary, of which 3,000 characters are frequently used in everyday life. A Chinese learner needs to know about 1, 000 characters with the highest frequency of appearance.

1. 可以说，所有的文字都是从图画开始的，但是图画并不等于文字。

2. "六书"学说揭示了汉字的来源，并能帮助人们在此基础上对汉字进行分类。"六书"即六种造字法，包括象形、指事、会意、形声、假借和转注。

3. 象形字来自象征性的图形。大多数象形字是独体字，由代表具体事物的图形演变而成。象形字大约只占汉字总数的3.9%，因为有很多抽象化的概念或行为难以用图形来代表。

4. 指事字是用标示性的符号来指明所要表示的意思。人们用抽象的符号或在象形字上添加笔画的方法来指明字义，如"本、末"。

5. 会意字是把义素组合在一起而形成的汉字。当需要表达一个较复杂的概念或事物时，可以把两个或两个以上的象形字合并使用，用它们组合的意思来表达。

6. 形声字包括两个部件：形符和声符。形符表示一个形声字所属的意义范畴，声符标示该字的发音。形声字在汉字中所占的比例最高，超过80%的汉字属于形声字。

7. 假借字是借用现有汉字的字形和字音而形成的表示不同意思的新字。

8. 转注字是指某些字虽然发音有些差别，但有相同的部首或近似的字义，从而可以从一个字转为另一个字。

Chapter Three

1. It could be said that all of the writing systems started from pictures. However, pictures are not equivalent to the writing system of languages.

2. The *liushu* theory explains the origins of Chinese characters, and classifies all characters based on the six principles of writing. The six categories include pictographic, indicative, suggestive, pictophonetic compound, borrowed and etymological characters.

3. The pictographic characters are the symbolized pictures, most of which are single component characters that are derived from pictures of concrete objects. The pictographic characters only possess approximately 3.9% of the total characters, since there are many abstract concepts or activities that could not be easily represented in the pictorial forms.

4. The indicative characters are the abstract symbols to indicate the ideas they are meant to convey. It could be created by a pure symbol or by adding a stroke which carries an abstract meaning to a pictographic form. For instance, 本, 末 .

5. The suggestive characters are compound characters. They are formed by the association of ideas suggested from their simple constitute elements. When people need to express a complicated concept or things, they have to put two or more pictographic characters side by side to describe it.

6. The pictophonetic compound characters are the characters that consist of two elements: a pictorial radical and a phonetic radical. The pictorial radical indicates the general meaning to which the character belongs; the phonetic radical indicates how the character is to sound. It is the largest category of Chinese characters, and over 80% of the total characters belong to this category.

7. The borrowed words are the new characters that borrow the graphs and pronunciations of existing characters, but represent different concepts.

8. The etymological characters are the characters that have identical radicals and somewhat similar meanings, but with different phonetics.

1. 书写工具的特点直接关系到书法的表现形式，同时影响到中国书法独具特色的发展。

2. "文房四宝"指的是中国书法所使用的书写工具。

3. "文房四宝"包括笔、墨、纸、砚。

4. 在中国传统书法中，毛笔是最重要的书写工具。通过毛笔笔锋的运转，书法家的心灵得到延伸和表达。

5. 墨的使用可以追溯到5000多年前。

6. 很多书法家仍然喜欢自己磨墨，因为自己研磨的墨汁可以根据需要调整浓淡。另外，磨墨本身也是书法创作的一个过程，是集中精神、激发灵感和进行构思的过程。

7. 砚台的作用是通过墨的研磨而产生可供书写的墨汁。

Chapter Four

1. The features of the writing tools have influenced the form that Chinese calligraphy has taken, and have also stimulated the unique development of calligraphy in China.

2. The concept of the "four treasures" refers to the writing tools used in Chinese calligraphy.

3. The "four treasures" are the brush, ink stick, paper and ink stone.

4. The brush is the most important tool in traditional Chinese calligraphy. The brush is an extension of a calligrapher's heart that expresses everything through the brushwork.

5. The use of the ink stick can be traced back to 5,000 years ago.

6. Many calligraphers still prefer to make ink by themselves, since they can create the desired ink consistency according to their needs. In addition, they feel the absorbing process of grinding ink is one part of their calligraphy work that gives them concentration, inspiration and time to work out the composition of a calligraphic work.

7. The function of an ink stone is to grind the solid ink stick into a usable liquid for calligraphy.

1. 中国书法有七种主要的书体，分别是：甲骨文、金文、小篆、隶书、楷书、行书和草书。

2. 从汉字创造时开始，书法和大自然就紧密联系在一起。每个构形优美的汉字都能或多或少地在大自然中找到它的影子，具有自然的活力，反映着大自然的和谐和韵律。

3.

中国书法常用书体一览表

书 体	历 史	特 点
甲骨文	甲骨文是古汉字最早的书体，距今已有3000多年。刻写在兽骨龟甲之上，记录兽骨龟甲烧后自然龟裂的纹路，用于占卜。	每个字基本上由平直的笔画组成，笔画尾部有一点儿尖。
金文	周朝（公元前1046~公元前256）使用的书体。现存大多数出现在青铜器上面。	与甲骨文比较，大篆书体在折弯钩处出现圆形，笔画粗细不一。
小篆	公元前221年，秦始皇统一中国后下令规范化的书体。它以秦国原有的书体为基础，是建立在大篆基础上的更完善的书写系统。	小篆与金文相似，但是笔画粗细一致，字体变长。
隶书	汉代（公元前206~公元220）出现的取代小篆的书体。用毛笔书写，更为快捷容易。这种书体大多见于各种文本，如赋税、契约、统计等。	横画的末端向上扬起，称"刀笔"或"雁尾"。汉字的拐角由圆角变为方角，因而更容易书写。
楷书	大约出现于公元3世纪。它是各种书体中最容易辨认和书写的书体，学习书法应从楷书开始。	保留了隶书的简捷和笔画的粗细变化，但是字形更为灵活轻便。
行书	基本上与楷书同步发展。	与楷书相似，但是笔画之间出现连接，因而字体更自由、流畅。
草书	草书因书写形式而得名，就像大风吹过草丛，看起来纷乱却有内在的章法。在形式和功用上，草书带有速写的性质。	与楷书相比，字的笔画大大简化，不适合一般书写。书法家往往使用这种书体来表现抽象的艺术。

Chapter Five

1. There are seven mainly used scripts of Chinese calligraphy. They are bone and shell script, bronze script, the small seal style, the clerical style, the regular style, the running style, and the grass style.

2. There has been a close relationship between calligraphy and nature ever since the characters were created. A well-written character in Chinese calligraphy must somehow resonate with the forms found in nature; it will possess force, as well as reflect the harmony and vital rhythm of nature.

3. An outline of the script styles of Chinese calligraphy

Script Style	History	Characteristics
Bone and Shell Script (also known as Oracle Bone Inscription)	The earliest known examples of Chinese writing are inscriptions on animal bones and tortoise shells. They can be traced back to more than 3,000 years ago. They were the records of divinations.	Characters are composed of fairly straight lines with sharp endings.
Bronze Script	It came into use during the Zhou Dynasty (1046 B.C. ~ 256 B.C.). Many of the surviving examples come from inscriptions that were cast on bronze vessels.	Compared to the bone and shell script, characters are more rounded at the corners and show mixture of thick and thin strokes.
The Small Seal Style	The first unifier and emperor of China Emperor Qin Shihuang ordered the writing system standardized in 221 B.C. He used the writing style of his native state, Qin, as the model script of the empire. The small seal script was established on the foundation of the great seal script.	This style is similar to bronze script except the lines are all of an even thickness and the characters are elongated.
The Clerical Style	It replaced the small seal style during the Han Dynasty (206 B.C. ~ 220 A.D.). This style could be written more quickly and easily with a brush. Most samples of this script were found on official documents (tax records, deeds, census records, etc.).	Notice the upward tilt at the end of horizontal strokes ("knife stroke" or "goose tail"). It is somewhat easier to write with square corners.
The Regular (or Orthodox) Style	It was created bout 300 A.D. It forms the starting point of calligraphic training and is the easiest script to decipher.	This style preserves the clerical script's simplicity and modulation of line width, but is less formal and heavy in appearance.

(Continued)

Script Style	History	Characteristics
The Running (or Cursive) Style	It was developed about the same time as the regular style.	It is close to the "regular style" but features connective lines between the strokes. It allows for more freedom and fluidity of movement.
The Grass Style	It takes its name from its appearance. It is a style that in form and function resembles shorthand.	Greatly simplified forms of the regular style. Not for general use, but for the calligrapher who wishes to produce a work of abstract art.

1. 中国书法和绘画都强调运笔用墨的技巧，并且都起源于大自然。无论书法还是绘画，笔墨的运用都要反映大自然的和谐与韵律。一般来说，学习中国绘画之前应先学习中国书法。

2. 中国文人书法家对书法艺术有着独特的审美观。他们更着眼于自我风格和气质的表达，而不是直观的外在形式。这种审美标准对书法和绘画都适用。

3.
中国书法发展简史

朝　代	概　要	简　评
商朝 （公元前1600～公元前1046）	甲古文是最早期的中国汉字。古代中国人在书写汉字时展示了他们非凡的艺术追求和艺术天才。	甲骨文不仅是中国书法的开始，而且也是中国书法作为一门艺术并得到进一步发展的基础。
周朝 （公元前1046～公元前256）	大篆或金文是在甲骨文基础上发展起来的。它不仅展示了文化的进步，而且也显示了那个时期对书写的重视。	与甲骨文相比，大篆进步了很多。不仅看起来更加典雅，而且对后期的书法产生了很大的影响。
秦朝 （公元前221～公元前206）	小篆或石鼓文是在中央集权之后为了规范、简化和推广文字系统而创立的。标准化的字体成为中国书法发展史上的一个里程碑。	与大篆相比，小篆在字形上更加严整规范，在结构上也更趋于对称平衡，便于书写。
汉朝 （公元前206～公元220）	汉代出现了各种书体的雏形，但是最富有代表性的是隶书。隶书更加注重笔画的起笔与收笔，在艺术上有了更大的发展空间。纸的发明也极大地促进了书法的推广。	隶书由于不受笔画长短、粗细的限制，因而更加灵活，不仅外形庄重，而且提供了书写者展现自我精神和气质的空间。
唐朝 （618～907）	对书法艺术的重视促进了楷书、行书和草书等各种书体的成熟，这些书体在当时统称为"现代书体"。楷书成为最受欢迎也最规范的书体，一直流传至今。书法艺术在唐代受到广泛重视，深受大众喜爱。	唐朝国力鼎盛，促进了文化的发展。其间出现了不少卓有成就的书法家，其中最擅长楷书的有书法"六大家"，他们成为后世学习书法的楷模。
宋朝 （960～1279）	文房四宝制作技术的提高和活字印刷术的发明促进和普及了书法艺术。很多古帖得以印行。	宋朝的大多数皇帝都迷恋书法，书法在科举考试中也受到了很大的重视。
清朝 （1616～1911）	清朝政府为书法艺术的发展提供了良好的环境。随着大量青铜器的出土和甲骨文、钟鼎文的发现并刻印成书，对甲骨文和钟鼎文的研究也兴盛起来。	中国书法艺术在这一时期达到集大成的高峰，清代皇帝，特别是康熙、乾隆，不仅都是书法家，而且都大力提倡书法。

Chapter Six

1. It is because both calligraphy and painting stress the qualities of manipulating the brush and ink, and take their origins from nature origin. In either calligraphy or painting, the brush movement should reflect the rhythm of nature. Grenerally speaking, it is a common practice for students to learn the fundamentals of calligraphy before painting.

2. The Chinese scholar-calligraphers have gradually developed an exclusive aesthetic attitude towards calligraphy. They are more interested in individual expression and spirit than in immediate visual appeal. This aesthetic attitude is applied to both calligraphy and painting.

3.

An outline of the historical development of Chinese calligraphy

Dynasties	Major Developments	Comments
Shang Dynasty (1600 B.C.~1046 B.C.)	Bone and shell script, or *Jiaguwen*, was developed during that time. It was the earliest examples of script. Ancient Chinese demonstrated their artistic pursuit and talent in the structuring of these Chinese characters.	Bone and shell script is not only the beginning of Chinese calligraphy, but also the foundation for the development of Chinese calligraphy as an art form.
Zhou Dynasty (1046 B.C.~256 B.C.)	Great seal script, or bronze script was developed on the basis of bone and shell script. It shows the cultural progress and reveals the emphasis on writing during that time.	The style of great seal script is much more advanced than that of bone and shell script. It looks more elegant and has had great influence on the calligraphy of later time.
Qin Dynasty (221 B.C.~206 B.C.)	The small seal script, or *Shiguwen*, was established in order to clarify, simplify and promote writing after setting up the centralized government. The standardization of the writing system was a landmark of the development of Chinese calligraphy.	The small seal style is neater, more standardized and more balanced in structure and easier to write than the great seal script.

(Continued)

Dynasties	Major Developments	Comments
Han Dynasty (206 B.C.~220 A.D.)	Various styles emerged, but the representative style of calligraphy was the clerical script. With more emphasis on the beginning and ending of strokes, the clerical script gains more room for creativity. The development of papermaking technology also greatly promoted the calligraphy.	The clerical script is more flexible since it has no restrictions as to the uniformity of length or width of lines. The style looks not only solemn, but also allows calligraphers to show their spirit and characteristics.
Tang Dynasty (618~907)	The importance attached to calligraphy led script forms such as the regular script, the running script and the grass script to take shape, and they were collectively known as "modern script". The regular script, or *Kaishu*, became the most popular and standard style. It continues to be used today. Calligraphy was highly regarded and enjoyed great popularity.	A period of great prosperity influenced the development of culture. Many distinguished calligraphers arose. Six noted masters of the regular script have become the models for later generations of students.
Song Dynasty (960~1279)	The improvement in the production of the "four treasures" and the invention of character board printing methods promoted and popularized Chinese calligraphy. A great amount of writing scripts were copied.	Most emperors in this dynasty were infatuated with calligraphy. The civil service examination system was perfected and calligraphy was given due attention.
Qing Dynasty (1616~1911)	The Qing government created a favorable environment for calligraphy's development. With the unearthing of bronze vessels and the discovery of the bone and shell script and the bronze script in this period, many rubbings were made, and the study of oracle bone and seal scripts flourished.	The last feudal dynasty in Chinese history witnessed a collective prosperity in calligraphy and painting. Qing emperors, especially Kangxi and Qianlong, were not only calligraphers themselves but also advocated calligraphy.

1. 练习书法是一个可以伴随一生而且受益无穷的爱好。书法练习看似缓慢，却要求身心结合，通过自我调控和耐心磨炼来完善性格。初学者要做到平心静气，全神贯注和百练不烦。

2. 学习书法的"五正"包括心正、头正、身正、足正和笔正。这"五正"的功夫关系到书法学习能否成功。

3. 握毛笔的方法是直握毛杆，笔锋在书写时始终与纸面保持垂直。

4. 练习书法之前要做到的"三步"是：

（1）布置好桌椅；

（2）准备好书写工具；

（3）学习正确的执笔方法。

5. 要注意的"四个基本规则"是：

（1）笔画是汉字的建筑材料；

（2）每个汉字的结构就像一幅画或一个建筑；

（3）字与字之间应该是艺术的而不是机械性的排列；

（4）注意字与行之间的组合。

6. 根据欧阳询的论述，每个汉字的形状应该像一个体形健美匀称的人。

Chapter Seven

1. The practice of calligraphy is a lifelong and enjoyable process. It is a slow and thoughtful art, entailing control and patience. The beginner should have a peaceful mind and be ready to commit to concentration and repeated practice.

2. The correctitude of five skills includes the correctitude in the state of mind, in the positions of head, body, feet and brush when practicing calligraphy. It depends on the correctitude of five skills to achieve success in calligraphy.

3. The brush should be held vertically so that the point of brush never has a slant when coming in contact with the writing surface.

4. The "three steps" are:

   (1) Set the table in the correct position;

   (2) Prepare the writing tools;

   (3) Hold the brush correctly.

5. The "four common senses" to keep in mind are:

   (1) The strokes can be considered as the building materials of characters;

   (2) The structure of a character can be considered as an individual picture or a building;

   (3) The lines formed by characters can be an artistic production rather than a mechanical column;

   (4) There are not many variations in calligraphy composition.

6. The stance of a character should be like that of a well-built man according to Ouyang Xun's advice.

1. 中国历史上最伟大的书法家之一王羲之将所有的笔画归纳为八种。

2. 汉字"永"包括这八种笔画，称为"永字八法"。

3. 如果掌握了这八种主要笔画，就有了学习书法的基本功，就能尝试用不同书体书写或简单或复杂的各种汉字。每种笔画都有变体，而具体是哪种变体取决于该笔画在汉字中的具体位置。

4. 写"点"时，毛笔顺时针移动，形成一个比较柔和的三角形。书写的方法是：（1）用毛笔笔锋向上挑，（2）转用中锋，（3）向右下方移动，（4）按笔，（5）提笔，用笔锋完成。

5. 写"横"画时，（1）用毛笔笔锋轻按在纸上，（2）往下按笔，而毛笔并不移动，（3）用中锋向右移，（4）笔锋行至"横"画的尾部，（5）提笔锋，然后向右按笔，（6）用笔锋向反方向提笔。

6. 写"竖"画时，（1）用毛笔笔锋向上移，（2）停顿一下，转笔锋向下，按笔，（3）轻提笔，用毛笔中锋向下移，（4）在竖画尾部顿笔，（5）提笔，用毛笔笔锋沿"竖"画反向运笔，收笔处应圆润而有力度。

7. "钩"画本身不是独立的笔画。写"钩"时，毛笔先按照写"竖"或"横"画的步骤（1）~（3）运笔，然后（4）提笔，（5）按笔，（6）提笔转锋，（7）慢慢提笔直到笔锋离开纸面，留下一个钩的形状。

8. 写"挑"画时，（1）下笔，（2）向下按笔，（3）向右按笔转锋，（4）从左沿45°角向右上方运笔，（5）渐渐提笔，直到出现一个尖尖的尾部。

9. 写"撇"画时，（1）用笔锋落笔，（2）转锋向右按笔，（3）向左下运笔，（4）慢慢提笔，形成一个像燕尾的向左下的撇画。

10. 写"短撇"时，（1）用笔锋向上运笔，（2）转锋向右按笔，（3）从右向左下运笔，（4）逐渐提笔，以一个尖形的尾巴收尾。"短撇"比一般的"撇"短，运笔快，形状像小鸟啄食。

11. 写"捺"时，（1）在左上方起笔，（2）开始轻轻向右下按笔，逐渐加压，笔画也逐渐加重，（3）呈倾斜形地向下运笔，直到右下角，（4）顿笔并按笔，（5）慢慢提笔，形成像刀锋一样的尖形。

Chapter Eight

1. Wang Xizhi, one of the greatest calligraphers in Chinese history, reduced all the strokes to eight basic components.

2. The Chinese character, *yong* (永; forever), contains the eight basic components. Also known as the "Eight Components of the Character *Yong* (永)".

3. Mastery of the key eight strokes provides an essential grounding for all forms of calligraphy, and allows beginners to form characters in any calligraphic style. Each of the eight strokes has variations, depending on its placement within the character.

4. The dot, or *dian*, is created by moving the brush in a clockwise circle, making a soft, triangular form. To make this stroke, (1) move the tip of the brush upward, (2) use the mid tip, (3) move downward to the right, (4) press downward, (5) complete the dot by lifting just the tip of the brush upward.

5. To create the horizontal, or *heng*, (1) touch the brush to the paper, allowing a slight drop as the brush makes contact, (2) press down briefly without moving the brush from the paper, (3) move the mid tip to the right, (4) reach the end of the stroke, (5) lift the tip upward, press the brush down to the right, (6) and finish by taking the tip of brush and moving backward.

6. To create the vertical stroke, or *shu*, (1) touch the tip of brush onto the paper and move upward, (2) pause for a moment, then turn the tip and press down, (3) lift the tip and pull downward, (4) at the end of the stroke, pause again, (5) finally pull the tip a little way back, retracing the line for a neat finish.

7. The hook, or *gou*, is created by steps (1)~(3) lower the brush onto the paper; briefly move it downward or horizontally as in the vertical stroke or horizontal stroke, (4) lift the tip, (5) press down, (6) tip the brush upward and turn right, (7) lift the brush cleanly off the paper to leave a neat hook shape.

8. To write the raise, or *tiao*, (1) touch the brush to the paper, (2) press the brush downward, (3) turn the tip and press to the right, (4) then move it at a of 45° from left to right up the page, (5) as you end the stroke, lift the brush off gradually to give it a sharp tip.

9. To write the left falling, or *pie*, (1) press the tip of brush downward, (2) turn the brush tip and press to the right, (3) move downward to the left, (4) lift the brush slowly to complete a short, swallowtail-like stroke.

10. To write the aside, or *duanpie*, (1) touch the brush tip to the paper, then press the brush upward, (2) turn the tip and press to the right, (3) move it from the right to the left and press down, (4) and lift the brush off gradually to give it a sharp tip. The aside is shorter than the left falling, and the brush moves faster. It looks like a pecking bird.

11. To write the right falling, or *na*, (1) begin at the top left, (2) proceed by pressing down very lightly to the right, gradually increasing the pressure on the paper to thicken the stroke, (3) move diagonally down to the bottom right, (4) pause and press at the base of the stroke, (5) gradually lift the tip to form a sharp and knife-like shape.

1. 大多数的汉字有一个以上的笔画，有的汉字甚至超过25画。

2. 学习者按照笔画的顺序来书写汉字，可以帮助记忆，而且书写得更自然、流畅。

3. 先横后竖：当一个汉字又有横画又有竖画的时候，要先写横画或由横画组成的笔画，后写竖画。比如：十、干。

4. 先撇后捺：当撇或捺相交或相连时，先写撇，后写捺。比如：人、大、文。

5. 先上后下：一般来说，先写上边的笔画，后写下边的笔画。比如：三、王、言。

6. 先左后右：先写左边的笔画，后写右边的笔画。比如：什、从、件。

7. 先外后内：当一个字上方有包围结构（包括左上方、右上方和左右上三方）时，先写外边的笔画，后写里边的笔画或被包围的笔画。比如：习、区、月。

8. 先进去，后关门：当一个字的四面都有包围笔画的时候，先写上方三面的包围笔画，再写被包围的笔画，最后写下面的关门封口的横画。比如：目、国、回。

9. 先中间后两边：当一个字的中间是以一竖画为中心，或者这个竖画与一横画相交，那么先写中间，再写左右两边。比如：小、水、业。但是，如果中心的竖画和其他笔画相交，竖画则应后写。比如：中、丰、半。

10. 不是。上述的笔顺规则应该综合应用。比如，基本规则是先横后竖，但是如果竖出现在横的左边，则要先写竖，后写横，比如：上、仁。另外一种情况是，横画在中间或下边并且是主要笔画时，应该最后写，比如：子、女、土。

Chapter Nine

1. The majority of Chinese characters contain more than one stroke. Some characters contain even more than 25 strokes.

2. It can help in the memorization of the characters and make the handwriting naturally and beautifully, if one can follow the stroke order.

3. "Horizontal" before "vertical". When a Chinese character has both horizontal and vertical strokes, first write the "horizontal" stroke and the strokes consisting of horizontal strokes, then write the "vertical" strokes, e.g., 十 and 干.

4. "Left falling" before "right falling". When the "left falling" stroke and the "right falling" stroke cross or join each other, first write the left falling and then the right falling, e.g., 人, 大 and 文.

5. From top to bottom. The upper stroke(s) should be written before the lower stroke(s), e.g., 三, 王 and 言.

6. From left to right. Write the stroke(s) on the left before the stroke(s) on the right, e.g., 什, 从 and 件.

7. From the outer to the inner. When a character is enclosed from the upper end (including upper left, upper right, and upper left to right), first write the enclosing strokes and then what is enclosed, e.g., 习, 区 and 月.

8. Inside before closing the door. When a character is enclosed on all four sides, write the enclosing strokes first, then what is enclosed, and finally the sealing horizontal stroke at the bottom, e.g., 目, 国 and 回.

9. The middle before two sides. When a vertical stroke is in the middle and in the prominent position or when it crosses a horizontal stroke, it should be written first, e.g., 小, 水 and 业. However, when a middle stroke crosses other strokes, it should be written last, e.g., 中, 丰 and 半.

10. No. The rules of stroke order should be applied in an integrated manner. For example, the general rule is to write the horizontal stroke before the vertical stroke, but when the vertical is to the left of the horizontal, the vertical precedes the horizontal, e.g. 上 and 仁. Another case is when the horizontal stroke is in the middle, or at the bottom, and takes a prominent position, it should be written last, e.g., 子, 女 and 土.

1. 汉字俗称方块字，每个汉字的笔画和部首都需要均匀地分布在一个方块里。 汉字的结构就像建筑，讲究对称的美。

2. 汉字的结构一般可分为两种：独体结构和合体结构。独体字仅有一个独立的部件，比如：水、木、手、口。合体字是由两个或两个以上的部件构成的，比如：好、学、这、国。

3. 合体字有三种主要结构：（1）左右结构，（2）上下结构，（3）包围结构。

4. 在所有的汉字中，左右结构的汉字最多，而上下结构的汉字第二。这两种结构的汉字大约占总汉字总字数的85%。

5. 依照左边部件和右边部件的相对大小，左右结构的汉字又可以分为三个小类：（1）左小右大， 比如：你、汉，（2）左右两部分基本一样大，比如：的、以，（3）左大右小，比如：外、刻。

6. 上下结构的汉字也有三个次分类：（1）上小下大，比如：字、写，（2）上下两部分基本一样大，比如：是、名，（3）上大下小，比如：点、息。

7. 包围结构的汉字也可分为三个小类：（1）两边包围结构，比如：厅、可、这，（2）三边包围结构， 比如：同、医、凶，（3）四面全包围结构，比如：回、国、田。

Chapter Ten

1. Chinese characters are known as square-shaped characters, and the strokes and components of a character should be placed proportionally within the square. A character is like a building where one strives to achieve beauty and symmetry.

2. The structures of Chinese characters can be roughly divided into two types: single component characters and compound characters. Single component characters include only one complete and independent component, e. g., 水，木，手 and 口; compound characters include two or more components, e. g., 好，学，这 and 国.

3. There are three major structures in the compound characters:
   (1) left-right structure, (2) top-bottom structure, and (3) enclosed structure.

4. Of all the characters, the left-right structures are more numerous than those with top-bottom structures. Characters of these two structures account for 85% of all Chinese characters.

5. On the basis of the relative size of the left and right components, there are three sub-categories: (1) a smaller left part plus a larger right part, e.g., 你，汉; (2) two parts of equal size, e.g., 的，以; (3) and a larger left part plus a smaller right part, e.g., 外，刻.

6. There are three sub-categories: (1) a shorter top plus a longer bottom, e. g.,字，写; (2) two parts of equal length, e. g., 是，名; (3) and a longer top plus a shorter bottom, e. g., 点，息.

7. There are three sub-categories: (1) enclosed on both sides, e. g., 厅，可 and 这; (2) enclosed from three sides, e. g., 同，医 and 凶; (3) and enclosed from all four sides, e. g., 回，国 and 田.

1. 一般先学楷书，再学行书或其他书体。

2. 开始描摹以前，应注意下项事项：

    （1）准备好书写工具：笔、墨、纸、砚

    （2）布置好桌面：把毛笔、墨、砚放在便于拿放的位置，如果右手执笔，把这些放在桌子的右边。

    （3）磨墨或用墨汁：平心静气，集中精神。

3. "摹"的意思就是按照范例"描红"。传统上，初学者把薄纸放在要学习的字帖上，然后按照字帖的范例把字描摹出来。

4. "双钩"是一种新的描摹方法，即把要勾勒的汉字的字形印出来，然后让初学者按照轮廓填摹。

Chapter Eleven

1. It is generally agreed that the regular style (*Kaishu*) should be learned first followed by the running style (*Xingshu*) or other writing styles.

2. Keep the following process in mind before you begin your brushwork:

    (1) Prepare the materials: the brush, ink stick, paper and ink stone.

    (2) Set up the table. Put the brush, ink stick, and ink stone within easy reach. If you are right-handed, place on the right side of the table.

    (3) Grind the ink or use ready-made ink. If you can, you should grind the ink by yourself, since it allows time to prepare your mind and heart for the work at hand.

3. *Mo* means tracing the model work. Beginners traditionally put a thin piece of paper over the characters they are going to learn, and then writing the character out according to the model work.

4. *Shuanggou* is a new way of tracing. The outlines of the Chinese characters are printed out, and beginners are required to just fill the inside.

1. 临帖是书法中最常用的一种练习方法。

2. 临帖的方法可以训练初学者眼和手的配合，加强对笔画、字形结构的了解，培养出对书法作品好与坏的分辨鉴赏能力。

3. 在开始临帖以前，要做好下列几件事：（1）选好字帖，（2）把字帖放在桌子的左边，（3）仔细揣摩每一个要临摹的字，（4）认真分析每个字的结构及每一笔的位置和写法，（5）模仿字帖上的一笔一画开始书写，尽量相似。

4. 长期以来，最流行的楷书字帖是书法大师颜真卿的颜体、柳公权的柳体、欧阳询的欧体和赵孟頫的赵体。颜、柳、欧阳为唐代的书法家，赵为元代的书法家。初学者可以根据自己的爱好选择，集中精力先练习其中一种书体。

Chapter Twelve

1. The most common way for learners to practice Chinese calligraphy is to copy model works.

2. It can train learners' hands and eyes to cooperate by copying model works. It can also strengthen their understanding of strokes and structures, and cultivate their appreciation of calligraphy works.

3. A learner should: (1) select a piece of model work that he or she likes most; (2) the model piece should be placed on the left side of the table before copying; (3) contemplate each of the model characters to be copied; (4) analyze each structure and the placement of strokes; and (5) copy every single stroke and character of the model work as accurately as possible.

4. The most popular model works in regular script (*Kaishu*) are Yan style created by Yan Zhenqing, Liu style by Liu Gongquan, Ou style by Ouyang Xun and Zhao style by Zhao Mengfu. Yan, Liu and Ouyang were calligraphers from Tang Dynasty, and Zhao was from Yuan Dynasty. A learner can choose and focus on any one of the styles according to his or her preference.

1. 经过描摹、临帖等阶段的练习后，就可以开始尝试脱帖练习。学习者可以根据自己学习、掌握的某一种书体，尽量尝试去完成一幅全新的书法习作，而不是简单复制某位书法家的作品。

2. 学习者可以根据自己的喜好，选取一首诗歌或一幅对联，或抄录一段文章，按照自己对书写内容的领悟和掌握的书法技能来书写。

3. 在脱帖练习时需要注意：

    （1）遵循正确的笔画顺序；

    （2）发挥好运笔技巧；

    （3）考虑好每个笔画在汉字中的位置；

    （4）安排好每个汉字在整幅书法作品中的位置。

4. 脱帖练习中常见的四种毛病，即"书法四病"是：

    （1）牛头：起笔时顿笔太重或着墨太多；

    （2）鼠尾：收笔时太轻，没有笔力；

    （3）鹤膝：拐弯时顿笔太重而形成粗重的"接口"；

    （4）蜂腰：两头粗中间细。

Chapter Thirteen

1. After tracing and copying model works, you may begin freehand practice. You should try to create a new piece of calligraphy work using the style that you are familiar with instead of copying the works of other calligraphers.

2. You can pick a poem, a couplet, an idiom or a passage to write according to your preference and your own understanding.

3. When doing freehand practice, you must keep in mind of the followings:

   (1) Follow the correct stroke orders.

   (2) Apply the skills of your brushwork.

   (3) Arrange the placement of each stroke in its own place.

   (4) Create each character in proportion with the whole of your work.

4. There are four common errors that should be avoided when you do the freehand practice.

   (1) "Bull head". You write with too much ink or pause too heavily at the beginning of each stroke.

   (2) "Rat tail". The ending part of a stroke is too thin and lacks strength.

   (3) "Crane's knee". When a stroke turns, the joint part is too big or thick.

   (4) "Hornet's waist". Both ends of a stroke are big with a thin body.

1. 生活中有很多不同类型的朋友。欣赏一幅书法作品就像与它建立长期的朋友关系。有的作品你会一见钟情，而有的作品你会随着时间而逐渐了解它的价值。事实上，一个人越懂中国书法，就会越喜爱书法艺术。

2. 印刷体不允许每个字的笔画和结构出现一丝一毫的变化，而书法家却不允许千篇一律。书法作品中的一笔一画都蕴涵着大自然的勃勃生机，反映出每个书法家不同的精神和气质。

3. 一幅好的书法作品往往包括两个方面：书写的内容与书写的风格。好的书法作品是内容与形式的结合体。了解书法作品的内容能够帮助领悟书法艺术的神韵，而抒发内在情感与志趣的文字也必然需要最恰当的书写风格来体现。

4. 鉴赏书法作品可以从以下六个方面来看：

    （1）和谐：大自然是一个统一体，书法作品也要像大自然那样，和谐地融合，形成一个完美的整体。

    （2）变化：变化是宇宙万物运转的基本规律。书法的艺术性也要通过错落变化来表现。

    （3）连贯：连续性无时无刻不存在于我们的生活之中。这些周而复始的互为依存的连续性同样要体现在书法作品中。

    （4）动感：动和静是万事万物存在的两个方面。中国书法要展现"动中有静、静中有动"的神韵。

    （5）均衡：阴与阳的平衡是万事万物中最重要的。书法艺术不但要追求均衡，也要追求在不均衡之中找到均衡。

    （6）韵律：韵律是在连续变动中自然形成的一种节奏和模式。书法家的才能就是要把大自然中的韵律转化到书法作品中去。

Chapter Fourteen

1. There are many kinds of friendships in our lives. Enjoying a good piece of calligraphy is similar to having a lasting friendship. You may fall in love at first sight, and learn more about its true value over time. The more you understand calligraphy, the more you will come to appreciate it.

2. Printing does not admit the slight variation in shape and structure. However, this stiff regularity is not to be tolerated by Chinese calligraphers. Every character of a fine calligraphy work reflects the energy of a living thing and a calligrapher's personal characteristics and spirit.

3. A masterful piece of Chinese calligraphy is a combination of two parts: content and style. It is very helpful to know the contents if you want to have a deep understanding of the spirit of a calligrapher. However, the content used to convey such emotions and spirit need the most appropriate calligraphy to deliver accurately and artistically.

4. The "six elements" to consider in the appreciation of Chinese calligraphy are as follows:

   (1) Unity. The universe is a unified entity. This is also true of calligraphy.

   (2) Change. Change is the basic process of the whole universe. Artistic quality of calligraphy should reflect those changes.

   (3) Continuity. Continuous motion is very evident in our life, and the principle of continuity should be demonstrated in Chinese calligraphy.

   (4) Motion. Motion and tranquility are two opposing phenomenon that are visible everywhere in the world. Chinese calligraphy should exhibit the feeling of "tranquility in motion and motion in tranquility".

   (5) Balance. The balance of *yin* and *yang* is extremely important in the world. Calligraphy seeks balance, and unbalanced balance is the aim of a calligrapher.

   (6) Rhythm. Rhythm is the active process of continuous movement to an organized pattern. A calligrapher should attempt to transpose nature's rhythm into his or her calligraphic work.

1. 书法不仅是视觉艺术，而且可以表现出书法家的思想和精神风貌。书法的应用范围十分广泛。我们可以运用学到的书法技能来创作，通过特殊的艺术手段来表达自己的情感。

2. 如果能用中国书法在贺卡上写下自己的祝福，那么不仅富有艺术的气息，而且接受贺卡的人也会感受到这份关爱。

3. 现在，越来越流行在T恤衫或其他纺织品上印染上表现书法艺术的汉字。这种方式不仅能表达个人的情趣志向，而且具有个性化的感人效果。

4. 在历史古迹上，常常可以看到知名书法家在石碑或匾额上留下的墨宝，这是中国的文化传统之一。这些书法佳作不仅带有强烈的艺术效果，而且与周围的历史景观交相辉映，给人们留下深刻难忘的印象。

5. 我们可以选择一个古代或现代的成语、格言或谚语，用中国书法的形式书写成条幅。可以是富有哲理的、励志的内容或表达追求和希望的话语等。

6. 对联一般指一对相互对偶的语句，上下句字数相等，意思互相补充。上下句对应词的词义和词性也都相对或相近。中国家庭常常喜欢选择对联的形式来表达他们的志趣或对生活的追求和祝愿。

7. 书法、诗歌和绘画传统上被认为是中国最主要的三大艺术。用秀丽飘逸的书法写下一首中国诗歌，可以进一步表达这首诗歌的情感和意境。书法家可以把诗歌的韵律转换成书法的韵律，从而把词语的美和书法的古雅融合为一体。

Chapter Fifteen

1. Not only is calligraphy a visual art, it also conveys a calligrapher's ideas and spirit. Chinese calligraphy is applicable to many occasions. You can use your calligraphy skills to work on projects and express your emotions with a special artistic appeal.

2. If you can present your words in Chinese calligraphy on a greeting card, the card will not only have artistic appeal, but will also show your care and love for the recipient.

3. A more and more popular use for calligraphy is to write characters on T-shirts and other fabrics. It is an impressive way to show your ideas and give your clothing a personal touch.

4. It is a Chinese tradition to have stone steles or scribed boards by famous calligraphers at historical and important places. These calligraphic works with their powerful artistic effect usually match well with the natural surroundings and make the places well-known and leave deep impressions upon viewers.

5. We can choose an idiom, a phrase or a proverb of classic or modern Chinese that appeals to you to write down as a banner in Chinese calligraphy. The contents of the phrases could be philosophical, motivational, hopeful or wise.

6. Couplets refer to a pair of diametrically opposing statements with the same number of characters and complementary content. Words with similar or opposite meanings or parts of speech are usually used in couplets. It is a common practice for Chinese people to choose couplets that can serve as their life maxim, wish or inspiration.

7. Calligraphy, poetry and painting are traditionally considered the three major arts in China. An elegant use of calligraphy is to write down a Chinese poem in order to further express the feeling and the spirit of a poem. A calligrapher can try to transpose a poem's rhythm into calligraphic rhythm in an attempt to combine the beauty of words with the elegance of the calligraphic form.